# Molecular Resonance Effect Technology: The Dynamic Effects on Human Physiology

by

## Dr. Howard Fisher, B.Sc., B.Ed., D.C.

## &

## Dr. Igor Smirnov, M.S., Ph.D.

The publisher does not advocate the use of any particular health care protocol, but believes the information in this book should be available to the public. The publisher and authors are not responsible for any adverse effects or consequences resulting from the use of any of the suggestions, preparations or procedures discussed in this book. Should the reader have any questions concerning the appropriateness of any procedure or preparation mentioned, the author and publisher strongly suggest consulting a well-informed professional health care advisor.

First published in Canada in 2008 by
**Britannia Printers Inc.**
Toronto, Ontario  M4E2V8

Fisher, Howard, Dr.
Smirnov, Igor, Dr.
Molecular Resonance Effect Technology:  The Dynamic Effects on Human Physiology
Includes bibliographical references.
ISBN 978-0-9780331-8-7

This book has been written as an educational tool. It is based upon a concensus of current facts contained in peer reviewed literature and the experience of the authors. This book is not intended to be used for the purposes of diagnosing or treating diseases. The information provided herein should not replace the advice of your caregiver. Always consult your chosen informed health care practitioner for concerns of any symptoms or active disorders.

# Table Of Contents

# Table Of Contents

# Table Of Contents

# Table Of Contents

# Table Of Contents

# FOREWORD

For those of you who have read any of my previous books, you will realize that I am somewhat of a health zealot. I have my five 'pillars' of health to which I subscribe in order to optimize physiological well-being as well as clarity of mind. Proper diet, supplementation, exercise, meditation (spirituality), and protection against environmental elements such as contaminated air, water and electromagnetic radiation are the categories that I feel merit our concentration to improve our health.

In September, I lectured at the A.A.C.L. (Anti-Aging Conference London) in England at the Royal Society of Medicine. It is at these conferences where the cutting edge of medical science, as it pertains to anti-aging, is revealed. Here is a shocking revelation for those of you who choose to lay the onus of poor health on heredity. Despite the fact that a major portion of disease was once believed to be based on genetic predisposition, the completion of the human genome study in 2003 has allowed researchers to reveal that the opposite is true. Eighty-five to ninety-six percent of all disease is due to environmental causes.[1] The impact of Professor Baranova's statement is based on her expertise in genomics, the study of the human

---

[1] Baranova H. New Look on Anti-Ageing Medicine through Genomics and Evidence Based Medicine. What Can Be Done In Practice. 4th Annual Anti Ageing Conference London 2007 (AACL) The Royal Society of Medicine. September 16, 2007.

genome, and in fact, her findings should make us realize that we have to become more aware of the environmental challenges to our health. I have known of Dr. Igor Smirnov's work with restructuring water for several years. I have been a strong advocate of the use of this water to optimize health, and you shall see, as the facts are unveiled, with good reason. Although his polymeric water activation does not purify water, the molecular resonance effect technology does maximize the beneficial capacities of this vital fluid. With the knowledge that we have gained from Dr. Baranova's genomic information, the MRET activated water can be used to our advantage to potentially counter these negative environmental effects.

Dr. Smirnov's breakthrough with water activation has led him to discover yet another polymer, perhaps the most protective element known to date in the midst of our ongoing crisis to combat the damaging effects of electromagnetic fields. In this book, Dr. Smirnov and I will attempt to enlighten and inform you about the derived benefits of molecular resonance effect technology.

Dr. Howard W. Fisher

# CHAPTER 1

# THE MOTHER OF INVENTION

*"The cell is immortal. It is merely the fluid in which it floats which degenerates. Renew this fluid at intervals; give the cell something on which to feed (nutrients) and, so far as we know, the pulsation of life may go on forever..."*

**Dr. Alexis Carrel**
**Winner of the Nobel Prize**

Whether the general population is aware of it or not, water is not water. The buzz in the media lately has been how both Pepsi and Coca Cola have been purifying tap water and selling it as bottled water. The times have changed, and both these corporate giants have seen the need to grab a piece of the ever increasing water market. In reality, this is just smart fiscal opportunism. Finally, a significant segment of society actually realizes the need for high quality potable water. The inherent lack of trust in the tap water delivered throughout the municipal pipelines of the world is now being evidenced, such as the recent findings in Toronto, Canada. In Toronto, several public schools have lead levels in the drinking water so elevated that the students have been banned from drinking it.

The physiological importance of water cannot be overlooked. We may think of water as the liquid that quenches our thirst, but this bi-polar fluid is responsible for hydrating cells, delivering nutrients, digestion, eliminating metabolic wastes, nutrient assimilation, respiration and maintaining the integrity of the total anatomy of the body. As a matter of fact, water is involved in every bodily function and the proportion of body composition is staggering. Although the overall fraction of the body is seventy to seventy-five percent water (70%-75%), human blood is approximately ninety percent water (90%). The brain is roughly eighty-five percent (85%) and muscle tissue is seventy-five percent (75%) water.[2] Any force that has the ability to affect water, can affect the body and its functions.

Just recently the actual structure of naturally occurring water had been established. The formerly accepted theory of water as a "tetrahedrally (pyramidal) coordinated random network is now replaced by a structural organization that instead strongly favors hydrogen-bonded water chains or large rings embedded in a weakly hydrogen-bonded

---

[2] Batmanghelidj F. Your Body's Many Cries for Water: A Preventive and Self-Education Manual for Those Who Prefer to Adhere to the Logic of the Natural and the Simple in Medicine. Global Health Solutions. Falls Church, VA. 1995.

disordered network."[3]  Scientists now believe that this structure best explains some of the phenomenal abilities of water, but even so, the bonds between the molecules of water are very transitional, lasting no more than a femto-second at best.[4]  Water is constantly in transition.  In other words, all the hype about clusters of five or six water molecules having particular properties now must rely upon some other explanation for the attributed properties.

Thanks to the work of the Japanese investigator Masaru Emoto,[5] we are beginning to understand that the structure of water can be changed, not only by the geomagnetic fields that vary diversely over the planet, but by the energy of thought as well.  The bipolarity of water has been long established and the subsequent changes to bonding angles are not only plausible, but a regular occurrence.  Using electromagnetic fields, there are subtle electrical effects that can be used to alter or modify the molecular structure of water and subsequently affect the properties and the ensuing physiological functions of this life-sustaining liquid that makes up more than seventy percent of the human body.  We must consider the fact that since we know this does occur, some water will be more physiologically beneficial, and on the other hand, some will be less beneficial due totally to the

---

[3]Head-Gordon T, Johnson M E. Tetrahedral structure or chains for liquid water. *PNAS*. 2006; (103)21: p. 7973-7977.
[4] Ibid.
[5] Emoto M, Thayne T A (translator).  The Hidden Messages In Water.  Beyond Words Publishing.  Hillsboro, Ore 2004.

changes in the water structure and the correlated changes in ensuing functions. It has been known for centuries that water is not water. Masaru Emoto has shown that water from different geographical areas will demonstrate a different crystalline structure when flash frozen and examined under the microscope. This is no doubt due to a diversity of geo-magnetic fields present at various locations around the world. The best looking crystals come from water found in the great spas of the world such as Lourdes in France. They used to be referred to as healing water. In fact the structure of water can actually be changed by human thought processes, also demonstrated by Emoto.[6]

The real objective is to find the water that optimizes or promotes the optimization of the physiological function of the body. "Water profoundly influences all molecular interactions in biological systems. The existence of life depends critically on the capacity of water to dissolve polar molecules that serve as … information carriers." [7]

For centuries this has been the quest of humanity, and some of the most famous spas in the world have developed around the 'healing waters' of Lourdes, France, Karlovy Vary in the Czech

---

[6] Emoto M (Thane D A translator). The Hidden Messages in Water. Beyond Words Publishing. Hillsboro, Oregon 2004.
[7] Stryer L. Biochemistry 4th Edition. Stanford University. CITY.1995.

Republic, the natural springs an hour into the hills outside Panama City, or the famous spas that surround Buda and Pest in Hungary. In these areas, the waters promote improved health and wellness and not merely by placebo effects. There are diagnostically proven documented changes.[8]

The challenge is to determine which changes to the structure of water will produce the most advantageous physiological responses and affect the body in a way as to promote overall health. Often it is the anomalous finding that leads the investigator down a path that may not have been an obvious deduction.

In 1986 Dr. Smirnov was part of the investigative team that was looking into the disaster at the Chernobyl nuclear power plant. There was a significant finding inside the affected perimeter: one group of irradiated people undergoing the rehabilitation in the health care facility in the area of mountain springs was not suffering from cancer, although millions of others were. This was the seed from which sprouted one of the most innovative molecular changes that we have seen to the structure of water.[9]

As you shall see in the following chapters, all water is in indeed not water. Structural changes

---

[8] Andreassi L, Flori L. Mineral water and spas in Italy. *Clinics in Dermatology*. 1996;(14)6:p. 627-632.

[9] Smirnov I. Activated Water. *Electronic Journal of Biotechnology*. 2003;(6)2:p.128-142.

do take place with the use of subtle electromagnetic fields and profound physiological benefits are commensurate with these changes.

# CHAPTER 2

# THE MRET WATER FINGERPRINT

*"The molecular structure of water is the essence of all life."*

*Dr. Albert Szent Gyorgyi*

The insurmountable nature of trying to reproduce the water that could apparently have an effect on cancer and other diseases may seem to have been an impossible mission. Whether it was a testimony to genius, or purely a serendipitous occurrence, apparently Dr. Smirnov proved equal to the task.

From his research into the Chernobyl disaster, Dr. Smirnov determined that it was the specific molecular structure of the spring water from the Caucasus Mountains that helped people to counteract to the development of oncological diseases following the adverse effects from the radiation. This finding was not uncommon because weak electromagnetic fields have the ability to change the properties of water[10] and therefore geo-magnetic fields from different regions of the planet have the ability to affect the structure and subsequent physiological effects of water as well. From Emoto's work, the evident changes in the water's molecular structuring can be corroborated.

After researching the effects of electromagnetic radiation on cellular structures at St. Petersburg University in Russia, Dr. Smirnov developed a system called Molecular Resonance Effect Technology (MRET) for the modification of the molecular organization state of water and other liquid substances. It took just under fifteen years from the disaster at Chernobyl for the United States patent office to issue the patent for the MRET activation device and the subsequent activated liquids produced.

The theory behind the creation of MRET activated water is soundly vested in the laws of physics. The effect an electromagnetic force has on an atom depends on the atom's electronic structure during the interaction. One could imagine that the application of the appropriate time-dependent force to an atom could alter its electronic structure in a specific way, thereby controlling its response to subsequent radiative or collisional processes. Furthermore, the specificity of certain reactions of the electronic structure might be used to reconstruct

---

[10] Semikhina L P, Kiselev V F. Effect of weak magnetic fields on the properties of water and ice. *Russian Physics Journal*. 1988;(31)5:p.351-354.

the motion of the atomic electron cloud. The key to the manipulation of electronic structure in atoms is the generation of electromagnetic fields or radiation that will push and pull the electronic wave function in a controlled and reproducible way. Thus, by controlling the dynamic parameters of the electromagnetic field it is possible to alter the structure of the fluid in a controlled manner, which may lead to the physiological effects of this fluid. The key is, of course, reproducibility.

It should come as no surprise to learn that what Dr. Smirnov has done through his molecular resonance effect technology (MRET) has changed the actual molecular composition of water so that the structure and frequency are similar to intracellular water. Not only that, the electrical properties are modified and predispose a more ideal ion exchange (proton pump) across the cellular membrane. Add to this the decreased physiological viscosity and surface tension, and now we have a mechanism to deliver nutrients and bring out intracellular toxins. Nuclear magnetic resonance spectroscopy has shown this water to be structurally different post-activation as well as UV luminescence spectrophotometry.[11] The level of physiological activity of MRET water is high.

A number of scientific investigations have demonstrated that the modification of the water's

[11] Vysotskii V I, Smirnov I V, Komilova A A. Introduction to the Biophysics of Activated Water. Universal Publishers. Boca Raton, FLA. 2005.

molecular structure caused by the MRET activation can ameliorate physiological and biochemical processes and positively influence cellular bio-structures. MRET activated water is produced through a non-chemical patented process using Molecular Resonance Effect Technology. This process of water activation induces the reformation of the molecular structure resulting in a molecular structure similar to intracellular water.

Furthermore, another of the premises behind molecular resonance effect technology is the direct transmission of pre-recorded molecular activity signals to biological systems (any person or animal) using the MRET activated water. One might consider these messages to be functional frequencies imprinted in water during the process of activation which may be carried out by the water with specifically modified long-range molecular structure. The subsequent effects of the activated water on bacteria, viruses, and abnormal cells, can be explained by the fundamental physical phenomenon of electromagnetism, such as; resonance, constructive and destructive interference.[12]

Water has been thrust into the limelight lately and there has been an elevated interest in reducing toxins, micro-biological pathogens, and assorted impurities. There are many types of purified waters such as spring, distilled, reverse-

---

[12] Berg J M, Tymoczko J L, Stryer L. Biochemistry 5th Edition. W. H. Freeman. New York. 2002.

osmosis, ionized, colloidal, and nano-clustered waters. However no process has previously been known which can alter the molecular structure of water without any foreign substances being introduced into the water.[13] [14] [15]

The critical factor in the manipulation of the electronic (molecular) structure of atoms is the generation of the electromagnetic fields, or radiation that will push and pull the electronic wave function in a controlled and reproducible way.[16] The water molecule has a polar triangular structure with the covalent bonding of two hydrogen atoms to one oxygen atom with a measured 104.5 degree angle between these bonds.

Water is one of the most polar molecules known in nature. The polarity of water underlines its chemistry and thus the chemistry of life. Polar molecules interact with one another through attraction. This weak attraction is called a hydrogen bond. In regular water, polar molecules form short-range, unstable associations of different crystal shapes. The process of MRET water activation induces the formation of long-range water

[13] Dunning F B. Rydberg Atoms- Giants of the Atomic World. Science Spectra. 1995;3:p.34-38.
[14] Gallagher T F, Beams J W. Rydberg Atoms. Cambridge University Press. New York. 1994; p120-135.
[15] Smirnov I. Activated Water. *Electronic Journal of Biotechnology.* 2003;(6)2:p.128-142.
[16] Jones R R. Modifying Atomic Architecture. *Science Spectra.* 2000; 22:p.52-59.

molecular domains similar to the water molecular structures found in living cells.

## HOW DOES ACTIVATION OCCUR?

The water-activating device used in Molecular Resonance Effect Technology (MRET) is made of a polar polymer compound mixed with specific amounts of pharmacologically active organic and inorganic substances. During the activation process, the MRET polymer compound is placed within an externally generated distinct electromagnetic field. Specifically, the MRET polymer compound is exposed to a homogenous magnetic field and an oscillating optical light with a wavelength of 600-700 nanometres and a frequency of 7.8 Hertz.[17]

As a result, the MRET compound generates very subtle, low frequency electromagnetic oscillations similar to those healthy geomagnetic fields found in specific areas on Earth such as the Caucasus Mountains in Europe or the Tibetan Mountains in Asia where the waters have been shown to provide dynamic changes to physiological functions. The naturally occurring water in these regions has been shown for centuries to improve health, support healing, promote longevity, and help eliminate heavy metals, allergens and other toxins and from living organisms.

---

[17] Vysotskii V I, Smirnov I V, Komilova A A. Introduction to the Biophysics of Activated Water. Universal Publishers. Boca Raton, FLA. 2005;p.134.

Consistent with the MRET theory, the applied electromagnetic field generates an excitation in the fractal geometry nano-ring structures of the MRET polymer compound. Due to the phenomenon of piezoelectricity and intensive electrical activity of the fractal nano-rings, this polymer generates biologically active subtle electromagnetic oscillations. During the process of activation, the water is affected by specific patterns of subtle, low frequency, pro-biotic electromagnetic oscillations emitted by the MRET compound. The process of activation modifies the hydrogen-bonding patterns of water molecules and induces the formation of the long-range multilayer molecular structures compatible with the intracellular water structuring. These results were confirmed by experimental work described in this monograph.[18]

As complicated as the MRET activation process may seem, all you must realize is that the activation process does indeed restructure the water. The following findings will show the structural differences between the control water (source water) and the MRET activated water: dispersion staining microscopy, nuclear magnetic resonance spectrometry, viscosity testing, and high voltage photography.

---

[18] Vysotskii V I, Smirnov I V, Komilova A A. Introduction to the Biophysics of Activated Water. Universal Publishers. Boca Raton, FLA. 2005.

## DISPERSION STAINING MICROSCOPY

Early in this book, the work of Masaru Emoto was mentioned. Emoto used a freezing technique to show different structural changes to water caused by geo-magnetic fields, pollutants and different energies.[19] The use of a similar technique (dispersion staining microscopy) has shown differences in the images of the crystalline structures in frozen water samples of the control and the MRET activated water. The water is frozen with a liquid nitrogen injection and then examined under polarized light. The structure, thickness and incident angle of the light will affect the diffraction of light off the crystals.

The figures represented here are micrographs from testing conducted at Meixa Tech Laboratories by analyst Bryan Burnett. The crystalline structure of the frozen tap water shows extensive irregular fracturing and chaotic crystalline formation (Figure I). This may be due to the impurities and poorly organized molecular structure of the tap water which have interfered with the crystallization process.

The MRET activated water sample shows well organized crystalline formations with a strong tendency of the crystal axis to be oriented in one direction. This difference in the structure is a result

---

[19] Emoto M (Thane D A translator). The Hidden Messages in Water. Beyond Words Publishing. Hillsboro, Oregon 2004.

## FIGURE I
## DISPERSION STAINING MICROSCOPY
## TAP WATER

## FIGURE II
## DISPERSION STAINING MICROSCOPY
## MRET WATER

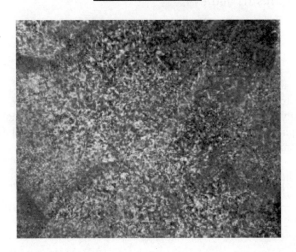

of the modified molecular structure of MRET water
( Figure II).

## NUCLEAR MAGNETIC RESONANCE

Nuclear magnetic resonance spectrophotometry has been shown to differentiate even the
most subtle difference between molecules,[20] and
therefore is an excellent modality to demonstrate
the difference between MRET activated water and
the control source water. Nuclear magnetic
resonance imaging is an excellent tool for validating
and determining differences in water structures.[21]

Dr. Lin Chiang conducted the Nuclear
Magnetic Resonance testing at NuMega Resonance
Laboratory in San Diego, California. The test
showed a consistent two and a half time (2.5-fold)
increase in the width of the proton peak in the line
of NMR absorption in MRET activated water
(Figures III and IV).[22]

---

[20] Salem A A, Mossa H A, Barsoum B N. Application of
nuclear magnetic resonance spectroscopy for quantitative
analysis of miconazole, metronidazole and sulfamethoxazole
in pharmaceutical and urine samples. J of Pharmaceutical &
Biomedical Analysis. 2006; 41(2):p.654-661.

[21] Jhon M S. The Water Puzzle and the Hexagonal Key.
Uplifting Press Inc. U.S. 2004;
[22] Smirnov I V. Activated Water. *Electric Spacecraft Journal.*
2002;33: p.15-17.

The narrow proton peak of the control sample of water shown in Figure III demonstrates a proton reactivity level that is extremely different from the results that are observed when testing the MRET activated water.

## FIGURE III
## NUCLEAR MAGNETIC RESONANCE TEST
## CONTROL

**Regular Water**

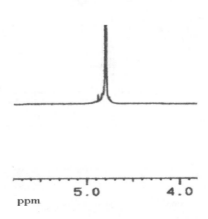

The water sample shown in Figure IV was activated for thirty minutes. The increased width measured in the proton peak could only have been caused by the modification of the shape of molecules and molecular structure of the activated water. This demonstrates another tangible measurement where the difference between the initial control water and the activated MRET water can be visibly noted and reproduced upon subsequent NMR testing.[23]   These results were produced by Dr. Leroy Lafferty in the Department of Chemistry laboratory at San Diego State University.[24]

## FIGURE IV
## NUCLEAR MAGNETIC RESONANCE TEST
## MRET ACTIVATED WATER

**Activated Water**

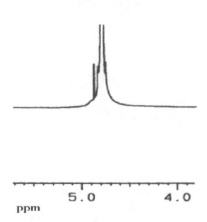

5.0          4.0
ppm

## HIGH VOLTAGE PHOTOGRAPHY

High voltage photography, sometimes referred to as Kirlian photography, is a method for

---

[23]Smirnov I. Activated Water. *Electronic Journal of Biotechnology.* 2003;(6)2:p.128-142.
[24] Vysotskii V I, Smirnov I V, Komilova A A. Introduction to the Biophysics of Activated Water. Universal Publishers. Boca Raton, FLA. 2005;p.138.

detecting energy variations in an object. A high voltage is briefly applied to a discharge plate to make the photographic exposure. The corona discharge (electron flow) between the object and discharge plate passes through and is recorded onto the film. When the film is developed you have a high voltage photograph of the object. One of the prime uses of this photographic technique is to show changes in energy patterns.

The high-voltage photography showed that the MRET activated water demonstrated an enhanced Corona Discharge Effect – luminous fringes that appear around the electrically conductive samples of water (Figures V and VI). The physical process of cold emission of electrons is responsible for producing the Corona Discharge phenomenon.

By examining the following two figures, the control water (before MRET activation) and the activated water, one can see that the increased emission of electrons in the activated water is visibly more intensive. The increase in the corona discharge effect is more than double, indicating that the water has a higher energy level.[25]

---

[25] Smirnov I. Activated Water. *Electronic Journal of Biotechnology.* 2003;(6)2:p.128-142.

## FIGURE V
## HIGH VOLTAGE PHOTOTGAPHY

**Regular Water**

## FIGURE VI
## HIGH VOLTAGE PHOTOGRAPHY

**Activated Water**

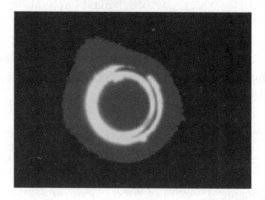

Since nothing was introduced to the water during the activation process to initiate the enhanced Corona increased electron release, it is reasonable to concede that proton activity in the MRET activated water has also increased.

## VISCOSITY

Gathering information about water's viscosity and the subsequent physiological behavior will allow us to understand the degree of difficulty or ease of the hydration or the permeation of the cellular membrane that will take place. Viscosity is defined as the measurement of the 'internal friction' of a fluid or the speed at which it will flow. The viscosity of any particular fluid, in this case water, defines the simplicity with which it may gain entry to the cell and to be used for absorption of nutrients or detoxification as well as for the hydration of the body. The relationship between hydration and aging has already been clearly established: aging is the progressive state of dehydration that occurs over time leading to an increase in cellular dysfunction. In other words, the more water we lose, the less efficiently we function.

The sophisticated scientific investigation showed that the viscosity of MRET activated water, when subjected to very low tangential pressure decreases up to 300-500 times compared to the non-activated water.[26] This research was conducted at

---

[26] Vysotskii V I. Investigation of Physical Properties of MRET Activated Water and its Successful Application for

Moscow State University, Russia using distilled water.    It is scientifically proven that cellular processes in biological systems are driven by the low energy of the bio-chemical reactions inside and outside the cellular structures. Consequently, these processes create low tangential pressures along water surfaces and cellular membranes.

Thus, the very low tangential pressures existing in biological systems contribute to the manifestation of the anomalously low viscosity of MRET water which results in improved intracellular/extracellular water exchange. This can contribute to the enhancement of the cellular transduction mechanism and the predisposition to optimal function of the cells in biological systems.[27]

The significance of this finding cannot be overstated.    Water is the delivery system for nutrients and the major vehicle for removal of cellular wastes.   By decreasing the viscosity of the water in the body structures, the potential for optimizing physiological activity has also been exponentially increased.

This decreased viscosity "means that the water has a 'super liquidity' characteristic and possesses very low resistance when it penetrates

---

Prophylaxis and Treatment of Oncology. Program and Abstract Book. International Congress on Medical Physics and Biomedical Engineering, August 27 - September 1 of 2006. Seoul, Korea. 2006.
[27] Smirnov I.V. The Anomalous Low Viscosity and Polarized-Oriented Multilayer Structure of MRET Activated Water. *Explore Magazine*. 2007;(16)4:p.37-39.

through small pores and capillaries in the body. Based on this fact, it is possible to conclude that MRET water may significantly improve the cellular membrane function as well as the physiological function of the circulatory system in the body."[28]

By using the verifiable, objective measurements of nuclear magnetic resonance spectrometry (increased width of the proton peak), viscosity testing under very low tangential pressure (300-500 times reduction in viscosity), high voltage photography (more than 100% increase in corona discharge) and dispersion staining microscopy (visible structural change), there is a clearly demonstrable structural change that has occurred from the control (pre-activated) liquid to the resultant MRET activated liquid. The truly exciting phenomena about the effects of the activation process on water are the irrefutable dynamic kinetic changes, not only on human physiological responses to the water, but to the suspension or reversal of many potentially pathological processes.

---

[28] Smirnov I V, Peerayot T. The Physiological Effect of MRET Activated Water. *Explore Magazine.* 2006;(15)1: p.38-44.

# CHAPTER 3

# THE PROOF IS IN THE LABORATORY

*"What I am going to tell you about is what we teach our physics students in the third or fourth year of graduate school... It is my task to convince you not to turn away because you don't understand it. You see my physics students don't understand it... That is because I don't understand it. Nobody does."*

**Dr. Richard P. Feynman, Nobel Prize winner and father of Nano-technology**

In September (2007), I attended the gala dinner for the Anti-Ageing Conference in London. This conference was located in the prestigious Royal Society of Medicine and sponsored by the lovely and gracious Mrs. Heather Bird-Tchenguiz. It is there that I found myself in the middle of a conversation with two of the other presenters: Dr. Robert Goldman, one of the founders of the medical anti-aging movement and the actor, Don Johnson. Both men looked great. Dr. Goldman, Chairman of the Board of the A4M (American Academy of Anti-Aging Medicine) had the inside track on all the current knowledge and looked as if he could still compete in the weight lifting competitions that were his forte in years gone by. Don, despite doing all his own tremendously physical stunts for years as Detective Crockett on the hit action show Miami Vice, appeared to be aging well. By his own admission he had picked up some of the anti-aging lifestyle insights and behavioral modifications to slow down the hands of time.

Our mere presence at this event availed us to the latest research findings of course because that is the nature of these cutting-edge conferences. However, Dr. Goldman as a founder and major domo in the world of anti-aging medicine was articulating on the future of anti-aging medical science. "We're close now. From what we know, if you can hang in another fifteen years in reasonable health, living one hundred and twenty to one hundred and fifty years should be attainable."

I thought back to the photos in National Geographic from the early 1970's taken in the Hunza Valley in Northern Pakistan. The photos of one hundred year-old men dancing spryly and the news of women giving birth in their seventies served to shift the aging paradigm that had become common place. This article was filled with pictures of robust active men doing the necessary life-sustaining chores needed to exist in a rugged rural environment, not really considered to be the 'norm' in western societies. The photographs also depicted women in their seventies, eighties and nineties carrying on the activities of daily life as if they were fifty years younger.

Dr. Henry Coandă, the Romanian genius who is considered to be the father of fluid dynamics, had linked the nature of the performance properties of the water that people drank with health benefits. He had investigated several areas in the world where the water-longevity relationship appeared to have a direct association. He was convinced that the secret of long life and good health lay in the water.

The similarities in the findings of Dr. Smirnov regarding the water from the Caucasian Mountain spring were now, not only echoing the previous work, but perhaps totally establishing the anti-aging link. After all, we now realize that aging is simply a manifestation of the on-going state of dehydration.

What other physiological changes were possible from altering the structure of water? The answer will astound you and so will many of the studies performed on mice. The well documented mouse genome study completed in 2002 and the report of the International Consortium's Mouse Genome Project cited that 99% of a mouse's genes have a function equivalent in humans and that their biological programming is startlingly similar.[29] The human genome study was completed in 2003, so we know the comparison to be valid.

---

[29] Epstein S S. The Stop Cancer Before it Starts Campaign. Chicago. The Cancer prevention Coalition. 2003;p.12.

The many benefits of MRET activated water
have been confirmed by extensive experimental
work conducted by investigators at universities,
independent testing laboratories and various
institutions around the world, including
immunology and oncology investigations on more
than 900 mice. To reduce the redundancy of
repetition throughout this chapter, several studies in
the animal (mice) model confirmed the optimal time
for MRET activation to be thirty minutes.[30]

As it was described in the previous chapter,
one of the basic concepts of MRET technology is
the direct transmission of imprinted molecular
activity signals (frequency) to plant and animal
biological systems through the medium of activated
water.[31]    During the MRET activation process,
water, or any liquid, is affected by subtle, low
frequency, pro-biotic electromagnetic waves which
are generated by the MRET polymer compound.[32]
They are similar to the healthy geomagnetic
frequencies found in several specific areas on Earth,
and as evidenced from the preceding chapter, are
able to modify the molecular structure of water,
making it very beneficial for living cells of both the
plant and animal kingdom. This concept is based on

---

[30]Smirnov I. Activated Water. *Electronic Journal of
Biotechnology*. 2003;(6)2:p.128-142.
[31] V ysotskii V I, Smirnov I V, Kornilova A A. Introduction to
the Biophysics of Activated Water. Universal Publishers. Boca
Raton, FLA. 2005:p.151.
[32] Smirnov I V, Trongawad P. The Physiological Effect of
MRET Activated Water. *Explore Magazine*.
2006;15(1):p.38-44.

the established relationship between certain frequencies (particularly the 7.8 Hz Schumann Resonance first harmonic) and their ability to provide pro-biotic benefits which can be transmitted to living systems through a medium such as a liquid due to a fact that water molecules participate in cellular communication and in principal metabolic functions.

## HYDRATION

In the previous chapter, we discussed the decrease of the viscosity (density) of MRET activated water subjected to very low tangential pressure when compared to non-activated water, which was established in the investigation at Moscow State University. This decreased level of the viscosity actually confirmed the long-range multilayer structuring of MRET water and its structural compatibility with intracellular water.[33] Such structure of water can contribute to the easier access of water through the aquaporins (cellular entry portals for water) in the singular manner required. The impact of this change is huge because the processes of disease and aging are related to dehydration, poor nutrition and toxic infiltration.

---

[33] Ling G N. A New Theoretical Foundation for the Polarized-Oriented Multilayer Theory of Cell Water and for Inanimate Systems Demonstrating Long-range Dynamic Structuring of Water Molecules. *Physiol Chem Phys & Med NMR*. 2003; 35: p.91-130.

The process of hydration was studied using an FDA approved Bioelectrical Impedance meter which measures changes in cellular conductivity, resistance and capacitance. Within twenty minutes, MRET activated water had entered the cells from outside the cells and the extra-cellular water (which we commonly refer to as edema or water retention) was reduced, thus improving cellular energy and function.[34] This test confirms the enhanced hydration ability of the MRET activated water. The control test on the non-activated water revealed the movement of water from outside to inside the cells within sixty minutes. It means that MRET water was absorbed in the body three times faster than the non-activated water. With the exception of MRET activated water, most types of drinking water can not be easy absorbed in the body, or in other words are not bio-available to living systems. Living organisms therefore have to metabolize (to structure) the water at great physiological energy expenditure, often at the expense of other functions.

Normally, molecules of water do not present with a linear organization and the body has to use energy to reorganize the structure of the water molecules to enable cellular absorption. This reorganization involves changing the bonding of water with structures and tissues and takes time. This action in all likelihood accounts for the significant decrease in absorption time for MRET

---

[34] Smirnov, I. "Activated Water," *Explore Magazine.* 2002;(11).2.

activated water since it is already organized in a structure that promotes absorption.

Since we have now shown that a vehicle exists that improves cellular function and hydration, what are the consequences? Increasing nutrient absorption, while decreasing cellular toxins, according to Nobel Prize winner, Dr. Alexis Carrel, promotes an increased state of health and cellular "immortality." With our aging population advancing in the development of degenerative, inflammatory and auto-immune disorders, the ability to enhance the hydration of the body is a monumental boon to increased functioning and decreasing pain.

The world is finally beginning to understand the rudimentary basis of nutrition, but sadly knowledge about detoxification is still lagging. Just so you fully understand the magnitude of the problem, we have currently reached the stage where xenobiotics, chemicals foreign to the biologic system,[35] are present in the adipose tissue (fat) of 100% of the population.[36] It is not like there is any shortage of potential toxicity with the constant presence of pesticides, thousands of food additives, heavy metals, pharmaceuticals, alcohol, tobacco,

---

[35] Friel J P, ed. Dorland's Illustrated Medical Dictionary. Twenty-fifth Edition. W.B. Saunders. Philadelphia. 1974.
[36] Gunderson E L. *FDA Total Diet Survey, April 1982-April 1986, Dietary intakes of pesticides, selected elements and other chemicals.* Food and Drug Administration, Division of Contaminants Chemistry. Washington, DC 20204.

caffeine and recreational drugs readily available for absorption in our environment, not to mention our own metabolic toxins. There is no speculation or guesswork because the evidence can be found by their presence in the blood, urines and feces. The function of all organs, tissues and the entire organism is dependent on the efficiency of the biological processing of the nutrient-toxicity relationship of the individual cell. Organs, such as the liver spend a major portion of their efforts trying to rid the body of these unwanted but environmentally available toxins.

When there is a toxic excess, the body stores these unwanted toxins in fat and generally fat deposits remain distal to the most important organs. MRET activation of water has demonstrated some astounding properties in both human and laboratory testing. The ability of this restructured water to help with detoxification and nutrient absorption alone may be extremely beneficial for overall health.

## MODIFICATION OF DIELECTRIC PERMITTIVITY

Dr. Vladimir Vysotskii, in his research at Moscow State University, found that MRET activated water subjected to an applied electromagnetic field of very low frequencies, caused the dielectric permittivity of water to be significantly decreased by eighty to ninety percent

(80% - 90%) compared to the non-activated water.[37] It is scientifically proven that cellular processes in biological systems are driven by the low energy of the bio-chemical reactions. Consequently, these processes create subtle, low frequency electromagnetic fields which contribute to the manifestation of the decreased dielectric permittivity of water in the body. The dielectric permittivity characterizes the resistance of water dipoles to the alignment with the electromagnetic field and it is directly correlated with the viscosity of water. Thus, the reduction of dielectric permittivity means that there is lower level of resistance to the alignment of water dipoles following the electromagnetic field. As a result the intracellular communication (the transduction of signals) based on the mechanism of the alignment of water dipoles with the electromagnetic fields is improved. The nature of the biofeedback mechanisms necessary to monitor homeostasis, hormonal levels, or organ system balance is dependent upon the optimization of intercellular communication. This is not a finding that will

---

[37] Vysotskii V I. Experimental Observation and the Biophysical Model of Strong Germicidal Activity of Water Activated with the help of MRET Process and Investigation of Physical Properties of MRET Activated Water and its Successful Application for Prophylaxis and Treatment of Oncology. Program and Abstract Book, International Congress on Medical Physics and Biomedical Engineering, August 27 – September 1, 2006, Seoul, Korea.

effect one particular organ or organ system but significant in that it will offer broad spectrum effects through many or even all systems.

## MRET ACTIVATED WATER EFFECTS ON STAPHYLOCOCCUS AUREUS

The bacteria, Staphylococcus aureus, has mutated to the extent that it began to show strains containing penicillin-destroying enzymes within three years after the introduction of penicillin in 1941.[38] Currently more than ninety-five percent (95%) of Staphylococcus aureus strains are penicillin resistant and methycilline resistant strains (MRSA) have become a plague worldwide.[39] "In 1992, 13,300 hospital patients died in the U.S. due to bacterial infections that resisted the antibiotics fired at them, says the CDC."[40] CDC studies indicate that this death rate estimation may be significantly higher,[41] and current estimates indicate approximately 103,000 die annually from MRSA infections in the U.S. alone.

The effects of MRET activated water on Staphylococcus Aureus infections *in vivo* in animal

---

[38] Neu H C. "The crisis in antibiotic resistance". Science. 1992; 257(5073): p.1064-73.
[39] Jacoby G A. "Antimicrobial-resistant pathogens in the 1990s". Annu Rev Med. 1996; 47: p.169-79.
[40] Begley S. "The End of Antibiotics". Newsweek. 1994; Mar. 28: p.46-51.
[41] Wenzel R P, Edmond M B. "The Impact of Hospital-Acquired Bloodstream Infections." Emerging Infectious Diseases. Vol. 7, No. 2. Mar-Apr 2001.

models were conducted at Kiyv (Kiev) National Shevchenko University, Ukraine by microbiology Professor, Dr. Lydia Kholodna. In this experiment four hundred mice were divided into groups. All mice were given an intra-peritoneal inoculation of cultured Staphylococcus aureus. Initially the experiment was designed to determine the time period of activation that was most effective in Staphylococcus aureus reduction. Thirty minutes of activation time was determined to be the optimum. The first group was the control group and they consumed only tap water. The two other groups of mice were given MRET activated water: the first group for two weeks and the other for four weeks previous to the onset of the experiment. To determine the level of active bacteria in each subject (mouse), a sample of fluid from the kidneys was drawn and cultured. Both groups of mice on MRET water had shown a significant decrease of pathogenic colonies after the initial twenty-four hours of the experiment.[42]

During the first nine days of the experiment, thirty percent (30%) of the control group died from the Staph. aureus infection. In the same time period not one mouse in either of the experimental groups (MRET activated water) died.[43]

---

[42] Kholodna L S. The Effect of MRET Activated Water on Staphylococcus Infections in vivo in Animal Model and in vitro on Staphylococcus aureus Wood-46 Culture. Biological Department of Kyiv National Taras Shevchenko University. Kyiv. 2007.
[43] ibid.

## FIGURE VII
## STAPH. AUREUS EXPERIMENT, CONTROL

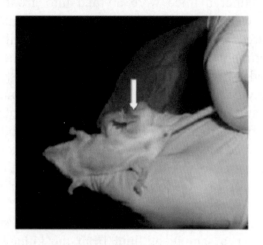

## FIGURE VIII
## STAPH. AUREUS EXPERIMENT, MRET

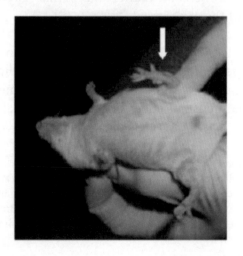

To determine the effects of the activated water on acute local inflammation, the inoculation site on the left rear paw was examined. On the control animals (Figure VII) an intensely reddened inflammatory reaction was observed on the surface of this paw (arrow points to the area), but on the experimental MRET water animals (Figure VIII) (arrow) there was no such reaction.

The conclusion to be drawn from this observation is that the regular consumption of MRET activated water not only has an anti-bacterial effect but contributes to the inhibition of the inflammatory response.

During the course of this experiment a number of analyses of the different immunological functions were conducted on the mice and some statistically significant findings came to light. After the first twenty-four hours, there was a considerable increase in phagocyte activity (an increase both in the number of phagocytes and their ability to digest bacteria) of the macrophages and neutrophils and in the activity of the lymphoid organs in the groups of mice that were drinking the MRET activated water.[44] These significant findings are indicative of an increased effectiveness in the immune system

---

[44] Kholodna L S. The Effect of MRET Activated Water on Staphylococcus Infections in vivo in Animal Model and in vitro on Staphylococcus aureus Wood-46 Culture. Biological Department of Kyiv National Taras Shevchenko University. Kyiv. 2007.

because these cell types are among the first line of defense. [45]

By bolstering the elements of immune response (cytotoxic macrophages, lymphocytes, T cells, monocytes, neutrophils, natural killer cells), it allows the body to elicit an appropriate response to any assault on the immune system. NK cells (natural killer cells) are the enforcers of the immune system, indiscriminately killing viruses and cancer cells on sight.[46]   Increased cytotoxic activity of lymphocytes enables the immune system to provide a more favorable first-line of defense response against any non-self intrusion, including chronic diseases and cancer.[47] NK cells function even if the immune cascade is compromised. These changes can be considered to be increased overall resistance.

The anti-bacterial effect of the MRET activated water has been corroborated in other experiments. A ninety-two percent (92%) reduction of Staphylococcus aureus was caused by MRET activation of a bacteria growth medium.[48]

---

[45] Ibid.
[46] Simone C. Cancer & Nutrition. Garden City Park, New York. Avery Publishing Group. 1992; p45.
[47] Imai Kazue, Matsuyama Satoru et al. Natural cytotoxic activity of peripheral-blood lymphocytes and cancer incidence: an 11 year follow up study of a general population. Lancet. Vol 356 Issue 9244. November 2000; p1795-99.
[48] Kholodna L S. The Effect of MRET Activated Water on Staphylococcus Infections in vivo in Animal Model and in vitro on Staphylococcus aureus Wood-46 Culture. Biological

Another study demonstrated the anti-bacterial properties of the MRET activated water by destruction of eighty-six percent (86%) of fecal coliform bacteria (Figure IX).[49] [50] The consistency of these results confirms the testing hypothesis that MRET activation of a liquid is able to suppress the growth of pathogenic microorganisms and thus is capable of sterilizing the fluid as well.[51]

## MRET ACTIVATED WATER EFFECTS ON ESCHERICHIA COLI

One of the most dangerous coliforms is Escherichia coli. The bacteria are very plentiful at the distal end of the digestive tract (colon) however it is extremely septic anywhere from the proximal end (mouth) to the stomach and can cause food poisoning and other infections. Fecal matter will contain E. coli.

A recent study on the effects of MRET activated water on Escherichia coli (E. coli) was

Department of Kyiv National Taras Shevchenko University. Kyiv. 2007.

[49] Smirnov, I. "Activated Water," Explore Magazine. 2002;(11).2.

[50] Vysotskii V I, Smirnov I V, Kornilova A A. Introduction to the Biophysics of Activated Water. Universal Publishers. Boca Raton, FLA. 2005.

[51] Kholodna L S. The Effect of MRET Activated Water on Staphylococcus Infections in vivo in Animal Model and in vitro on Staphylococcus aureus Wood-46 Culture. Biological Department of Kyiv National Taras Shevchenko University. Kyiv. 2007.

### FIGURE IX
### MRET ACTIVATED WATER EFFECTS
### ON TOTAL COLIFORMS COUNT

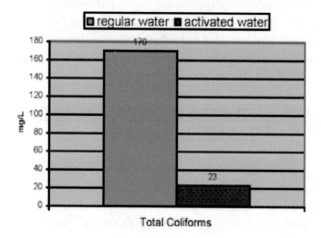

Total Coliforms

conducted at the Kiyv (Kiev) Institute of Microbiology and Virology of Ukrainian Academy of Science in both aerobic and anaerobic environments. The aerobic study demonstrated a major reduction in the growth of these bacteria. By activating the growth medium for thirty minutes, E. coli growth was inhibited thirty times (30-fold). Nutrient medium activated for sixty minutes increased the effectiveness of the E. coli inhibition by a factor of ten (300-fold).[52]

---

[52] Smirnov I V. The Effect of MRET Activated Water on Microbiological Culture Escherichia coli K-12 and on Complex Microbiological Associations. *Explore Magazine*. 2008; 17(1):p.1-6.

In the anaerobic study, simulating conditions in the lower colon (large intestine) where E. coli is part of the normal flora, there was no reduction in the bacterial count.[53] The presence of E. coli in the colon represents part of the integral balance necessary to keep other microorganisms from multiplying and creating imbalances which would disturb homeostasis and create disease processes as a result. The fact that the MRET activated water did not disturb this balance is just another positive physiological benefit of the structural changes to the water molecule.

The theory behind the anti-pathogenic effects generated by the MRET activated water postulates that these MRET electromagnetic fields interact with the abnormal fields generated by the DNA of mutated cells such as those found in viruses and bacteria. A destructive interference is created which suppresses the biochemical reactions in these cells.[54] [55] The potential possibilities for the anti-pathogenic effects of MRET activated water are endless as can be seen from some of the other viral studies.

---

[53] Ibid.
[54] Smirnov I V. Mechanism of\] Activated Water's Biological Effect on Viruses. *Explore Magazine.* 2003;(12)4:p.34-36.
[55] Smirnov I V. Activated Water. *Electronic Journal of Biotechnology.* 2003;(6)2:p.128-142.

## MRET ACTIVATED WATER EFFECTS ON HIV

One of the most destructive viruses to ever plague mankind has been the one to cause AIDS. Thailand is a nation in south-east Asia that for a number of reasons has a much higher segment of the population suffering for HIV infections. The clinical investigations and observations on patients suffering from AIDS were conducted at the Wat Phrabaatnamphu AIDS/HIV foundation just outside Bangkok, Thailand under the auspices of Dr. Peerayot Trongsawad.

In the clinical trial, the experimental group consisted of thirty-eight AIDS infected patients. Each patient had consumed one and a half liters of MRET activated water per day in conjunction with their prescribed antiretroviral (ARV) and pharmaceutical regimens. There was another group of AIDS infected patients who did not receive the MRET activated water, however they did receive their prescribed antiretroviral and pharmaceutical medications. These subjects were the control group. During the course of clinical observations, all patients, both in the control and experimental groups, were tested on a regular basis for CD4 counts and required to submit weekly subjective reports regarding their health conditions.[56]

---

[56] Smirnov I V. Clinical Observation by Peerayot Trongsawad, M.D., Using MRET Activated Water as Additional Treatment. *Explore Magazine.* 2006;(14)6.

Dr. Peerayot's clinical observations of the AIDS patients who were receiving the MRET activated water regimen revealed a dramatic increase of CD4 counts (ranging from an initial count of two (2) cells per milliliter to a final count of eight hundred and forty (840) cells per milliliter.[57] A normal reading is considered in the range of eight hundred (800) to twelve hundred (1200) cells per milliliter. Anything less is considered to be a dysfunctional immune system.

There was a dramatic decrease in the viral load (less than fifty) by most of the patients in this investigation. Viral Load is an indication of the level of virus infection in a body. Dr. Peerayot's observation of AIDS patients included the subjective evaluation and acknowledgement of any health improvements for both groups. More than ninety-four percent (94%) of the patients taking the MRET activated water described significant beneficial health changes. In contrast, there was no subjectively verified health improvement for any symptoms of the AIDS patients in the control group, and this is despite the fact that both groups were on antiretroviral therapy.[58] [59]

---

[57] Smirnov I V. The Physiological Effect of MRET Activated Water on Patients Suffering from AIDS. *Explore Magazine*. 2006;(15)2:p.37-40.
[58] Smirnov I V. The Physiological Effect of MRET Activated Water on Patients Suffering from AIDS. *Explore Magazine*. 2006;(15)2:p.37-40.

The Figure X is the picture taken of a man who is HIV positive and suffering from AIDS. He is one of the thirty-eight subjects in the experiment. His skin colour has turned much darker due to the effects of the disease on the liver. In a Caucasian individual the colour change would be more of a jaundiced yellow/green tinge common to liver failure and the inability of the body to carry out detoxification functions efficiently, if at all. He also appears swollen and inflamed throughout his body. Blood works revealed an extremely high viral load and very low CD4 counts.[60]

After the consumption of one and a half litres of MRET activated water daily for only eight days, radical changes occurred. In Figure XI (August 2004) skin colour changes reflecting improved liver function can be observed. The swelling that was apparent throughout his body has subsided significantly in an extremely short period of time.

The observations of the AIDS/HIV patients in this study continued for approximately one year from August 2004 to August 2005.

---

[59] Smirnov I V. Clinical Observation by Peerayot Trongsawad, M.D., Using MRET Activated Water as Additional Treatment. *Explore Magazine.* 2006;(14)6.
[60] Smirnov I V. Clinical Observation by Peerayot Trongsawad, M.D., Using MRET Activated Water as Additional Treatment. *Explore Magazine.* 2006;(14)6.

## FIGURE X
## MRET WATER EFFECTS ON HIV
## CONTROL

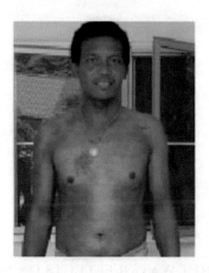

In Figure XII (July 2005), the same subject is shown almost eleven months after starting the MRET water consumption. From the initial appearance, the change is so dramatic that it is difficult to recognize the subject from his previous photos. There appears to be a cessation of the normal etiology of his HIV infection. From an outer appearance his overall inflammation has decreased and his skin discoloration from liver function has disappeared. His Viral load count dropped to below fifty and his CD4 count has risen to 840.

### FIGURE XI
### MRET WATER EFFECTS ON HIV
### TEN DAYS OF   CONSUMPTION

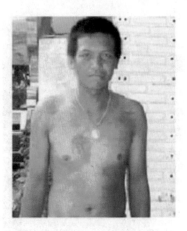

### FIGURE XII
### MRET WATER EFFECTS ON HIV
### ELEVEN MONTHS OF  CONSU\MPTION

## ACIDIC-ALKALINE BALANCE AND MRET
## WATER MEMORY

The pH scale is used to measure the acidity or alkalinity of any solution. It is a logarithmic scale that reflects the concentration of hydrogen ions in the solution expressed by reciprocals of the power of 10. The scale runs from zero to fourteen (0 to 14). Values less than seven (7) are in the acidic range; Values greater than seven (7) are in the alkaline range. A high pH value corresponds to a large negative power of 10, meaning a weaker concentration of hydrogen ions (alkaline). A low pH value indicates a small negative power of 10, which represents a high concentration (acid).

Pure water has a concentration of $10^{-7}$ hydrogen ions $(H^+)$ which equals the concentration of hydroxyl groups $(OH^-)$. This translates into a neutral pH factor of seven (7), which is neither acidic nor alkaline. Vinegar has a concentration of $10^{-4}$ hydrogen ions; its pH value is 4, which is acidic. Sodium hydroxide has a pH value of 14, which is alkaline extreme; hydrochloric acid has a pH value of 0, which is extremely acidic.

Investigative studies at Moscow State University, Russia and at CAI Environmental Laboratory in Carlsbad, California concerning pH, revealed that the thirty minute MRET activation had a tendency to balance the pH values of water closer to neutral pH=7.0 [61] [62] compared to non-activated water. The results may depend on the initial pH value of the water, the type and the source of water, the time of activation and a number of environmental conditions.

The research, which was conducted at Moscow State University on distilled water which had been MRET activated for fifteen (15), thirty (30), forty-five (45) and sixty (60) minutes, as well as on non-activated water, revealed the oscillating and fluctuating character of pH values. The results for the first four hours after the water activation are presented on Figure XIII and the results for the first sixteen days following the water activation are represented in Figure XIV.

The fact that the oscillating changes in the pH value can be observed not only for the first hours but even during several days (at least fourteen days in case of thirty minutes of MRET activation) supports the idea that the water can keep MRET

---

[61] Vysotskii V I, Smirnov I V, Kornilova A A. Introduction to the Biophysics of Activated Water. Universal Publishers. Boca Raton, FLA. 2005.

[62] Vysotskii V I. Experimental Observation and the Biophysical Model of Strong Germicidal Activity of Water Activated with the help of MRET Process and Investigation of Physical Properties of MRET Activated Water and its Successful Application for Prophylaxis and Treatment of Oncology. Program and Abstract Book, International Congress on Medical Physics and Biomedical Engineering, August 27-September 1, 2006. Seoul, Korea.

## FIGURE XIII
## MRET WATER EFFECT ON pH VALUES
## FOR THE FIRST FOUR HOURS

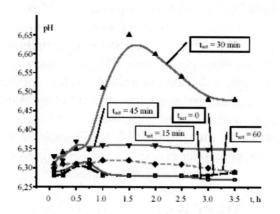

## FIGURE XIV
## MRET WATER EFFECT ON pH VALUES
## FOR THE FIRST 16 DAYS

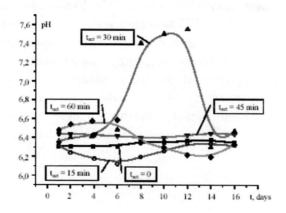

beneficial properties for several days at room temperature.

The results of this test confirm the scientifically valid phenomena of the existence of "water memory." In other words, the study verifies the ability of water to store information for a significant length of time. Another study involving oncological diseases in animal models conducted at Kiyv Institute of Experimental Pathology, Oncology and Radiobiology of Ukrainian Academy of Science confirmed the ability of MRET water to keep its health beneficial properties for forty-five (45) days when it was kept refrigerated at 0° C.

## MRET WATER ENHANCES THE DEVELOPMENT OF BRAIN TISSUES

In May 2005 an investigation was conducted at the Center for Research in Neurodegenerative Diseases at the University of Toronto under the supervision of Dr. Fraser. Dr. Fraser examined the effect of MRET activated water in transgenic mice with Alzheimer's disease. This research provided some evidence regarding an increase in the development of the brain tissues in the group of mice ingesting MRET water. The mean value of total brain area for the mice receiving the MRET activated water was increased by fifteen percent

(15%) when compared with the total brain area of the mice in the control group (Figure XV).[63]

## FIGURE XV
## MRET ACTIVATED WATER EFFECT ON
## THE BRAIN TISSUES

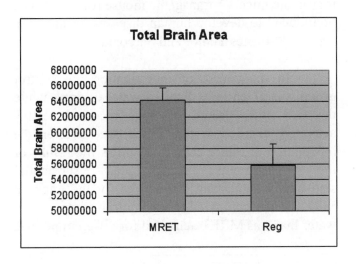

## ANTI-TUMOR EFFECT

A very exciting study involving MRET activated water was conducted on five hundred (500) mice at the Kiev Institute of Experimental Pathology, Oncology and Radiobiology, Ukranian Institute of Science under the supervision of Dr.

---

[63] Smirnov I V. The Physiological Effect of MRET Activated Water on Patients Suffering from AIDS. *Explore Magazine*. 2006;(15)2:p.37-40.

V.I. Vysotskii.[64] The purpose of this experiment was two-fold: to determine if the activated water was effective against cancerous cell growth, and if the initial hypothesis was true, to determine the period of activation that was the most effective in producing these results. This experiment involved transgenic mice. A transgenic mouse is one that can be induced to develop human diseases, in this case Ehrlich's Ascites Tumor and Sarcoma.

In the course of investigation the control group was given only distilled water to drink while the two other groups of mice received MRET activated distilled water. Three weeks after the inoculation of tumor cells to all mice, the results of the experiments demonstrated substantial statistically significant differences for the mice on MRET water compared to the control group.[65] The water that was MRET activated for different periods

[64]Vysotskii V I. Experimental Observation and the Biophysical Model of Strong Germicidal Activity of Water Activated with the help of MRET Process and Investigation of Physical Properties of MRET Activated Water and its Successful Application for Prophylaxis and Treatment of Oncology. Program and Abstract Book, International Congress on Medical Physics and Biomedical Engineering, August 27 – September 1, 2006, Seoul, Korea.
[65]Vysotskii V I. Experimental Observation and the Biophysical Model of Strong Germicidal Activity of Water Activated with the help of MRET Process and Investigation of Physical Properties of MRET Activated Water and its Successful Application for Prophylaxis and Treatment of Oncology. Program and Abstract Book, International Congress on Medical Physics and Biomedical Engineering, August 27 – September 1, 2006, Seoul, Korea.

of time (15, 30, 45 and 60 minutes) and MRET water which was kept in a refrigerator for forty-five days was able to affect tumor growth. The water that had been activated for thirty minutes was the most effective.

The substantial anti-tumor efficacy was confirmed by a very high level of reduction by seventy-six percent (76%) of the Total Number of Viable Tumor Cells in a 'preventive treatment' group and by fifty-five percent (55%) in a 'therapeutic treatment' group which received the thirty minute activated MRET water.[66] 'Preventive treatment' consisted of receiving MRET water during two weeks before and three weeks after the tumors had been induced. 'Therapeutic treatment' consisted of receiving MRET activated water only three weeks after tumors had been induced.

Furthermore, by the end of the experiment all surviving members of the control group were riddled and swollen with tumors (Figure XVI, A), however the mice from both groups on MRET activated water did not display any apparent swelling (Figure XVI, B).[67]

---

[66] Smirnov I V. MRET Activated Water and its Successful Application for Preventive Treatment and Enhanced Tumor Resistance in Oncology. *European Journal for Scientific Research.* 2007;16(40:p.575-583.
[67] Smirnov I V. MRET Activated Water and its Successful Application for Preventive Treatment and Enhanced Tumor Resistance in Oncology. *European Journal for Scientific Research.* 2007;16(40:p.575-583

## FIGURE XVI
## ERLICH'S SARCOMA TRANSGENIC MICE

## MRET WATER AND LONGEVITY

In this oncology experiment involving five hundred mice, statistically significant findings regarding longevity came to light. For the mice which received MRET activated water for two weeks prior to the inoculation of the tumor cells and during the three weeks after the tumors had been induced, the life span increased by sixty-one percent (61%). For the mice that received MRET water only during the three weeks after the inoculation of tumors, the life span increased by forty-three percent (43%).[68]

---

[68] Smirnov I V. MRET Activated Water and its Successful Application for Preventive Treatment and Enhanced Tumor Resistance in Oncology. *European Journal for Scientific Research.* 2007;16(40:p.575-583.

Earlier, Dr. John Stelle conducted in vitro laboratory testing to determine the effects of MRET activated water on several species of Lymphoma cells at the Laboratory of Engene Biotechnologies Inc. The different kinds of Lymphoma cells were incubated with the diluted MRET activated water for twenty-four (24) hours and demonstrated a consistent inhibition of growth of tumor cells by MRET water at ratio 1:10. The diluted activated water suppressed the metabolism of human cancer cells (BUC) by thirty-three percent (33%), canine cancer cells (Lymphoma 1308) by fifty percent

### FIGURE XVII
### MRET WATER VERSUS CANCER CELL
### GROWTH

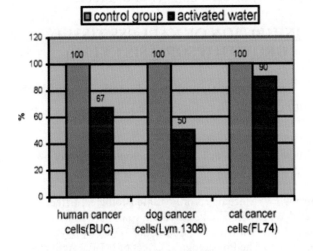

(50%), and feline cancer cells (FL74) by ten percent (10%) compared to control.[69]

An interesting comparison of activated water to the role of chemo-therapy in dealing with cancer must be brought to light. The goal of chemo-therapeutic agents is to destroy all elements of the cancerous (oncological) growth before the host dies. As strange as that may sound, it is unfortunately a very real phenomena. Usually chemo-therapy carries with it consequences and side-effects such as weakness and debilitation of the immune system to varying degrees and a host of other symptoms. There are no such negative side effects using the activated water, and as a matter of fact, all 'side-effects' are physiologically beneficial and positively affect a number of disorders.[70] [71] [72]

## INHIBITION OF KALLUSS TISSUE GROWTH (PSORIASIS CELLS)

In an experiment conducted at the Kiyv Institute of Plant Genetics of the Ukranian

---

[69] Smirnov I V, Peerayot T. The Physiological Effect of MRET Activated Water. *Explore Magazine.* 2006;(15)1:p.38-44.

[70] Smirnov I V. Mechanism of Possible Biological Effect of Activated Water on Patients Suffering from Alzheimer's Disease. *Explore Magazine.* 2006;5:p.53-56.

[71] Smirnov I V. The Physiological Effect of MRET Activated Water on Patients Suffering from AIDS. *Explore Magazine.* 2006;(15)2:p.37-40.

[72] Smirnov I V, Peerayot T. The Physiological Effect of MRET Activated Water. *Explore Magazine.* 2006;(5)1:p.38-44.

## FIGURE XVIII
## PSORIASIS, BEFORE

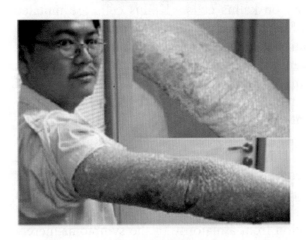

## FIGURE XIX
## PSORIASIS, AFTER 21 DAYS MRET
## ACTIVATED WATER USE

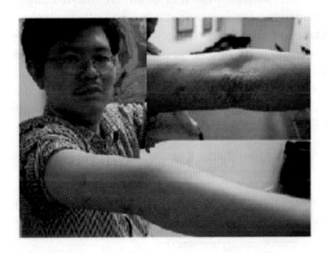

Academy of Sciences, Professor V. Vysotskii determined the effects of MRET activated nutrient medium on kallus cells. Kallus cells are mutated cells of botanical origin that have the ability to grow uncontrollably in a nutrient medium. Similar cells from animal sources are known as psoriasis cells. The investigation revealed that MRET activated water reduced kallus cells growth by ninety-three percent (93%).

This ability to inhibit kallus tissue proliferation is one of the possible explanations for the reason that several subjects who suffered from psoriasis have had such a quick and profound resolution from a majority of the symptoms merely by undergoing a regimen of drinking the MRET activated water and also spraying it on the skin lesions. In a study done in Thailand, a number of psoriasis suffers who had been on anti-histamine medication for several years had their lesions disappear in a few months.[73] In Figure XVIII one of the subjects in the study displays the psoriasis skin lesions on his arm. In only three weeks of the MRET activated water regimen, the skin lesions have responded remarkably and have virtually disappeared (Figure XIX).

## MRET WATER AND CHEMOTHERAPY

The goal of chemotherapy is to destroy tumors before causing significant irreversible

---

[73]Smirnov I V, Peerayot T. The Physiological Effect of MRET Activated Water. *Explore Magazine.* 2006;(15)1:p.44.

damage in the host organism. The clinical observation was conducted at Cedars-Sinai Comprehensive Cancer Center on the condition of a patient undergoing chemotherapy treatment for naso-pharyngeal cancer. This patient had been taking activated water for the course of his chemotherapy and the regimen had affected the immune system in a very positive manner.

In standard cases of chemotherapeutic intervention, the white blood cells count (WBCC) usually decreases to two to three percent (2%-3%) of a patient's pre-chemotherapy level (more than a ninety percent reduction), but in this case the decrease was only to five to nine percent (5%-9%) of the pre-chemotherapy levels. MRET water ingestion prevented the decrease of the WBCC to the normal lower levels and caused the rebounding of the WBCC to the pre-chemotherapy levels in only two to three days. This return to pre-therapeutic levels normally requires about three to five weeks.[74] This phenomenon bears further investigation since one of the major health issues in America today is the decreased immune system function.[75]

---

[74]Smirnov I V. Activated Water. *Electronic Journal of Biotechnology.* 2003;(6)2:p.128-142.

[75] Stoff J. An Examination of immune Response Modulation in Humans by Antigen Infused Dialyzable Bovine Colostrum/Whey Extract Using A Double Blind Study. Tucson. Immune Consultants. 2001.

# REDUCTION OF FREE RADICALS IN ACTIVATED WATER

Free radicals (ions) can affect cellu_ function in negative way. Consequently, the reduction of the level of free radicals in the body leads to the enhancement of the body homeostasis and metabolism. Testing conducted at C.A.I. Environmental Laboratory, Carlsbad, USA revealed the reduction of free radicals following the process of MRET activation. [76] [77]    This phenomenon is subject to further investigation. The results may depend on the type of free radicals, initial levels of concentration of free radicals in the water, the type and the source of water, the time of activation and a number of environmental conditions.

In the water activated for thirty minutes, the amount of calcium ions decreased by 72% and the amount of magnesium ions decreased by 18%. As a result, the hardness of water (combined amount of ions of calcium & magnesium) decreased by 45%. These results support the idea that free radicals (positive ions) bond with the long-range multilayer polarized molecular structures in MRET water and therefore have less effect on the process of proper cellular function. The decrease of the hardness in

---

[76]Smirnov I V. Activated Water. *Electronic Journal of Biotechnology.* 2003;(6)2:p.128-142.
[77] Vysotskii V I, Smirnov I V, Kornilova A A. Introduction to the Biophysics of Activated Water. Universal Publishers. Boca Raton, FLA. 2005.

MRET activated water contributes to its soft and smooth taste.

The process of activation increased the turbidity of water by eighteen percent (18%). The increase of turbidity illustrates that free radicals are bonding with long-range polarized molecular structures of MRET activated water and can form sediments.

## FIGURE XX
## MRET WATER HARDNESS TESTING

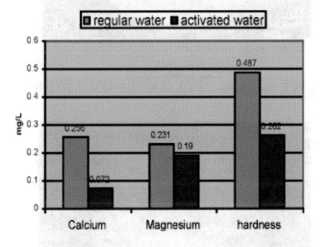

## MRET WATER INGESTION AND LIVE BLOOD CELL ANALYSIS

Live blood cell analysis was conducted by Dr. Vincent Seet at the Elixir Health Laboratory in Singapore using the darkfield microscopic techniques. In this figure below (Figure XXI), the

### FIGURE XXI
### LIVE BLOOD CELL ANALYSIS, BEFORE

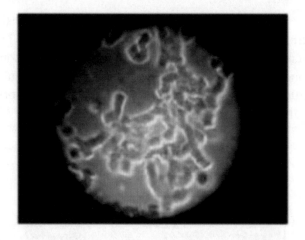

### FIGURE XXII
### LIVE BLOOD CELL ANALYSIS, AFTER

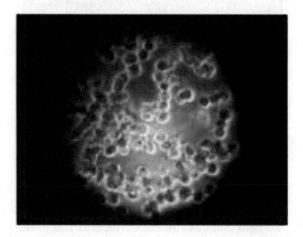

blood sample of the subject was taken before
MRET activated water was ingested. This sample

demonstrates Rouleau formations.[78] Rouleau are stacks of red blood cells which occur when the plasma protein concentration is increased. These clumped red blood cells (RBCs) are an indication that the ESR (erythrocyte sedimentation rate) is also increased. Conditions such as infections, inflammatory and connective tissue disorders, and cancers may display Rouleau. One of the complicating factors of Rouleau is that one of the functions of red blood cells is to deliver oxygen to all tissues in the body. When the red blood cells are stacked, they will not be able to travel down the smaller capillaries and arterioles and deliver their oxygen load. Often symptoms such as fatigue, shortness of breath and poor blood circulation resulting in a cold sensation in the extremities may occur. Twenty minutes after drinking the MRET activated water, most of the Rouleau patterns have been broken up, and the red blood cells can be seen as individual round spheres, now able to deliver the life-supporting oxygen load that they carry.

## ASSOCIATED MRET WATER ACTIVATION FINDINGS

Although the focus of this book is to deal with the effects of MRET Technology on human physiology, it is important to point out some of the other investigations. The examination of the effects

[78]Vysotskii V I, Smirnov I V, Kornilova A A. Introduction to the Biophysics of Activated Water. Universal Publishers. Boca Raton, FLA. 2005.

of MRET activated water on plant growth and germination was conducted during a three (3) month period at Kiyv Institute of Plants Genetics of Ukranian Academy of Science. In the course of this investigation it was observed that MRET water enhanced the growth cycle and accelerated the process of seed germination of several plants, particularly of cabbage, pumpkin, string beans, garden radish and pears.[79]

The process of MRET activation affects other liquids in a similar manner. In September 2007 a vineyard owner activated several different growth years of wines and conducted a comparison taste test. Her conclusion was that wine activated for thirty minutes had a decreased tannin taste, seemingly a more aged taste. No quantitative evaluation on tannin content was carried out, but her wine-tasters' consensus was that the wine improved in apparent value due to the differences in smoothness and taste.

## MRET WATER THERMOGRAPHIC STUDIES

Dr. Linda Fickes, a multi-talented physician and medical thermographer from Hawaii, has brought to light some amazing findings about the ability of MRET activated water to reduce cellular heating due to inflammatory conditions.

---

[79] Vysotskii V I, Smirnov I V, Kornilova A A. Introduction to the Biophysics of Activated Water. Universal Publishers. Boca Raton. 2005;p.149-150.

## FIGURE XXIII
## THERMOGRAPHY IMAGE
## OTITIS MEDIA BEFORE

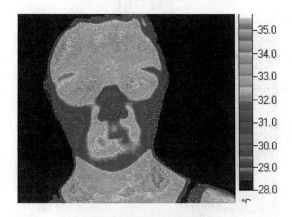

## FIGURE XXIV
## THERMOGRAPHY IMAGE
## OTITIS MEDIA AFTER

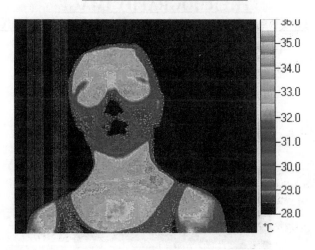

## FIGURE XXV
## THERMOGRAPHY IMAGE
## 10 YEAR OLD, RHINITIS INFLAMMATION
## BEFORE

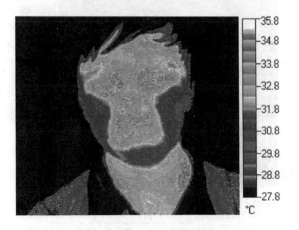

## FIGURE XXVI
## THERMOGRAPHY IMAGE
## 10 YEAR OLD, RHINITIS INFLAMMATION
## POST MRET WATER CONSUMPTION

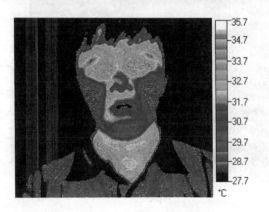

Figure XXIII shows a six year-old girl suffering from a right middle ear infection (otitis media). This will appear on the left side of the image in this book. Five minutes after consuming eight ounces of MRET activated water the image below (Figure XXIV) was captured. There is no longer any excess heat in the ear, mouth or sinus areas.

Dr. Fickes captured the following images of a ten year old boy with allergic rhinitis. Note the excessive heat in the sinus areas (frontal and maxillary), nasal regions and mouth. Inflammatory conditions cause an increase of extracellular fluids (edema) which consequently bring the following accelerated immune response. This activity accounts for the increased heat (temperature) in the areas seen in Figure XXV.

In Figure XXVI it is the image of the same ten year-old boy captured fifteen minutes after consuming twenty ounces of MRET activated water. It is a proven fact that consumption of MRET activated water decreases inflammation.

Recent studies have proven that the aging process and the progressive increase of body fat content contribute to the decline of the overall water content in the body. The average forty-five year-old man has retained a body content of approximately sixty-five to seventy percent (65%-70%) water, but an obese man of the same age will have only about forty-five percent (45%) water, and the water content of the average man by the age of seventy decreases to 45%-50%. [80]

These thermographic images demonstrate that there has been a significant decrease of the increased heating effects due to the reduction of the inflammatory condition of the rhinitis.

Using magnetic resonance imaging, Japanese investigators found out that aging results not only in dehydration, but that intercellular water undergoes significant structural changes: the amount of bio-water bound to biological macromolecules increases and the amount of "free" structured water decreases. [81] Consequently cellular communication, nutrient delivery, detoxification, oxygenation and other biological functions based on the dynamic interactions of bio-water decline with age. The process of transduction of bioelectrical signals into biochemical reactions (cellular communication) also declines, causing the commensurate break down of the cellular repair and replication mechanisms. This impacts upon the metabolic efficiency of the body. The hydration of the body tissues helps to improve the functions of cellular systems, to restore the metabolic competence and to support the process of

---

[80]Smirnov I V. Activated Water. *Electronic Journal of Biotechnology*. 2003;(6)2:p.128-142.
[81] ibid

rejuvenation.[82]    MRET activated water has demonstrated outstanding physiological and physical properties.[83] [84] This is all facilitated by the structural changes caused by the MRET activation of water resulting in a different molecular configuration of the water, the stronger hydrogen bonding and the changes to the molecular structures.

Another important benefit of the activated water is that living organisms do not have to use a significant energy expense to assimilate and metabolize the MRET activated water in order for it to be compatible with the recognized structure of cellular water. This allows all organs and tissues in the body to receive the necessary supply of structured water which will enhance and support their functions.

From the preceding investigations presented in this chapter, the findings show that these changes are able to eliminate a number of problems and as a result, beneficially affect individual health conditions and resolve many systemic health issues.

---

[82] Smirnov I V. Activated Water. *Electronic Journal of Biotechnology.* 2003;(6)2:p.128-142.
[83] Vysotskii V I, Smirnov I V, Kornilova A A. Introduction to the Biophysics of Activated Water. Universal Publishers. Boca Raton, FLA. 2005.
[84]Smirnov I V. MRET Activated Water and its Successful Application for Preventive Treatment and Enhanced Tumor Resistance in Oncology. *European Journal forScientific Research.* 2007;(16)4:p.575-583.

## TABLE I
## THE FUNCTIONS OF MRET ACTIVATED WATER

| |
| --- |
| Increased hydration |
| Increased nutrient absorption |
| Increased cellular detoxification |
| Enhanced immune response |
| Decreased inflammation |
| Anti-bacterial |
| Anti-viral |
| Anti-tumor |
| Inhibits growth of mutated cells |

# CHAPTER 4

# THE EMF CRISIS

*"Electromagnetic fields and radiation, damage DNA and enhance cell death rates and therefore they are a Ubiquitos Universal Genotoxic Carcinogen that enhances the rates of Cancer, Cardiac, Reproductive and Neurological disease and mortality in human populations. Therefore there is no safe threshold level. The only safe exposure level is zero, a position confirmed by dose-response trends in epidemiological studies"*

**Dr. Neil Cherry Associate
Professor of Environmental Health
Lincoln University, New Zealand**

Humans are electrical creatures. As a matter of fact, our neurological systems function by using electrical currents (cerebral cortex cortical tracts) and we are able to create our own endogenous electricity with no outside mechanisms involved (sino-atrial node of the heart).

Electromagnetic fields of assorted strengths and frequencies abound in our environment. When electricity leaves the energy production plant, it is clean 50 or 60 Hertz sine wave energy, however along the way it is affected by power surges (transients), radio frequencies (RF), and harmonics as it passes through electronic resistances and devices. The electricity gets chopped up into smaller segments, gathers high frequencies (RF), and spreads out to flow across wires, pipes and even the ground. The electrical energy generated by power plants has a lot of opportunity to pick up these frequencies. The energy leaves the generating facility and travels across high-voltage power lines and is then routed through transformers (which lower the voltage) and into individual homes. Electric and magnetic fields surround every aspect of this energy transmission.

EMFs (electromagnetic fields) are produced by the creation, transmission, and subsequent use of electricity by any device. In other words, power lines, electrical wiring, transformers and electrical equipment create this hazard, although the actual fields in your home are dependent upon many factors. EMFs also include Electro-Static Fields (fields that surround direct current), Radio Frequency (RF), and Electrical Noise. EMFs are also created by a transient phenomenon, which occurs whenever there is a dramatic burst of energy, such as a spark plug firing, lightning, or the motor brushes in an induction load (refrigerator, furnace fan, air conditioning compressor). These fields are the area of concern and more appropriately referred to as high-frequency, microsurge transients or 'dirty' electricity. The intensity of these currents fluctuates with the conductivity of the organ or tissue, but this energy can produce ionization of serum or cellular electrolytes and change body chemistry. EMFs' effects are on a cumulative basis, so awareness of your environment can help you make wise decisions. Current evidence from the top scientific investigators indicates that there are serious reasons for concern about the associated health risks from ELFs and RFs.[85].

Information started to leak out of the Soviet Union, where scientists have been studying about increased incidences of cancer, depression, cardiac anomalies and other health disturbances among the population affected by EMFs for over fifty years. According to Yuri Grigoriev, Chairman of the Russian National Committee on Non-Ionizing Radiation Protection, research on the biological effects of EMFs in the former Soviet Union has been ongoing for fifty years. Mr. Grigoriev advocates the belief that exposure to magnetic fields (EMFs) greater than two milliGauss (mG.) causes cancer.

In North America, one of the first investigations to report an association between cancer and power lines was published in 1979 by epidemiologist Nancy Wertheimer and physicist Ed Leeper. They reached the conclusion that children

---

[85] Sage C, Carpenter D, Eds. BioInitiative Report: A Rationale for a Biologically-based Public Exposure Standard for Electromagnetic Fields (ELF and RF). BioInitiative Working Group. USA. August 31, 2007; Section 1:p.3.

who died from cancer were two to three times more likely to have lived within forty metres of a power transmission line. EMFs (magnetic fields) were linked as a possible reason.[86]

After attending a major symposium on the health effects of electromagnetic fields held in Kazakhstan, American engineer Dr. Karl Maret commented, "There appears to be some confirmation that EMFs can have a significant impact on metabolic systems including elevated blood glucose levels, elevations in lipid levels, increased neuro-regulatory disturbances, decreased testosterone levels in males and impacts on the CNS, cardiovascular, and immune systems. In general, it appears that EMF stress leads to conditions of more rapid aging and the current proliferation of EMFs, especially the increased use of low-level microwave devices such as cell phones by our children, may have important socio-economic consequences."[87]

The startling reality is that most of us will be affected by magnetic fields virtually twenty-four hours per day. There are electromagnetic fields created in houses, cars and of course from the cell phone you are using while walking down the street. Think about it, EMFs are everywhere. No one can

---

[86] Wertheimer N, Leeper E. Electrical wiring configurations and childhood cancer. *Am J Epidemiol.* 1979; 109:p273-284.
[87] Maret K. Electromagnetic Fields and Human Health. National Foundation For Alternative Medicine. Washington, D.C. 2003; p17.

say for sure, but to ignore the apparent relationship is paramount to negligence.

No one has really told us exactly what potential threat EMFs possess. Many of us believe that headaches, heart disease, ADD, fatigue, aches, pains, allergies, digestive difficulties, mucus build-up and chemical sensitivities that affect a large percentage of the population are due to other causes. From an epidemiological perspective, the evidence is irrefutable. There are too many studies with positive findings for this health issue to be overlooked.

EMFs may manifest in a two hundred to four hundred percent (200% to 400%) greater risk of diseases such as cancer, leukemia, lymphoma, brain tumors, spontaneous abortions, Alzheimer's disease or suicide (of electrical workers).[88] [89] [90]

Another prominent Russian researcher, Prof. Valentina Nikiyina, author of, "Occupational and Population Health Risks of Radio Frequency Electromagnetic Fields," states that EMFs can cause

---

[88] Villeneuve P J, Agnew D A, et al. Non-Hodgkin's lymphoma among electric utility workers in Ontario: the evaluation of alternative indices of exposure to 60Hx electric and magnetic fields. *Occup Environ Med.* 2000; 57:349-357.
[89] Hillman D. Exposure to electric and magnetic fields (EMF) linked to neuro-endocrine stress syndrome: increased cardiovascular disease, diabetes and cancer. *Shocking News.* 2005; (8):p2.
[90] Wertheimer N, Leeper E. Adult cancer related to electrical wires near the home. *Int J Epidemiol.* 1982; 11:p345-355.

central nervous system, blood chemistry and cardiovascular system damage, with symptoms including angina, atherosclerosis, chest pain, digestive disorders, fatigue, headache, hypertension, insomnia, irritability, low blood pressure, sleep disturbances and many other cardiac and neurological pathologies.[91] She went on to indicate that the clinical findings from prolonged EMF exposure look like premature aging.

A group of international researchers combined their efforts to provide conclusive evidence that cells inside electromagnetic fields can activate certain signaling pathways that have been associated with cancer.[92] [93] Their results demonstrate that EMFs may change the biochemistry of the immune system that affects our degree of resistance to pathogens. The body of research consistently finds strong associations of

---

[91] Maret K. Electromagnetic Fields and Human Health. National Foundation For Alternative Medicine. Washington, D.C. 2003; p13.

[92] Dibirdik I, Kristupaitis D, Kurosaki T, Tuel-Ahlgren L, Chu A, Pond D, Tuong D, Luben R, Uckun F M. Stimulation of Src family protein tyrosine kinases as a proximal and mandatory step for SYK kinase-dependent phospholipase C Gamma 2 activation in lymphoma B-cells exposed to low energy electromagnetic fields. *J Biol Chem.* 1998; 273:p4035-4039.

[93] Kristupaitis D, Dibirdik I, Vassilev A, Mahajan S, Kurosaki T, Chu A, Tuel-Ahlgren L, Tuong D, Pond D, Luben R, Uckun F M. Electromagnetic field-induced stimulation of Bruton's tyrosine kinase. *J Biol Chem.* 1998; 273:p12397-12401.

EMF effects beyond random chance.[94 95 96 97 98] A Swedish study in the early 1990's by Feychting and Ahlbom (1993) demonstrated a 1.7 times higher risk for leukemia in adults and a 2.7 times higher risk for childhood leukemia.[99] Several studies indicate an increased incidence of cancer due to EMFs.[100 101]

---

[94] Wertheimer N, Leeper E. Adult cancer related to electrical wires near the home. *Int J Epidemiol.* 1982; 11:p345-355.

[95] Poole C, Trichopoulis D. Extremely low-frequency magnetic fields and cancer. *Cancer Causes Control.* 1991; 2:p267-276.

[96] Adey W R. Evidence for tissue interactions with microwave and other nonionizing electromagnetic fields in cancer promotion. In Fiala J and Pokorny J (eds). Biophysical Aspects of Cancer. Charles University. Prague. 1987.

[97] Draper G, Vincent T, Kroll M E, Swanson J. Childhood cancer in relation to distance from high voltage power lines in England and Wales: a case controlled study. *BMJ.* 2005; 330:p1290-1295.

[98] Baris D, Armstrong B G, Deadman J, Theriault G. A mortality study of electrical utility workers in Quebec. *Occupational and Environmental Medicine.* 1996; 53:p25-31.

[99] Feychting M, Ahlbom A. Magnetic fields and cancer in children residing near Swedish high voltage power lines. *Am J Epidemiol.* 1993; 138:p467-481.

[100] Washburn E P, Orza M J, Berlin J A, Nicholson W J, Todd A C, Frumkin H, Chalmers T C. Residential proximity to electric transmission and distribution equipment and risk of childhood leukemia, childhood lymphoma, and child hood nervous system tumors: Systematic review, evaluation, and meta-analysis. *Cancer Causes Control.* 1994; 5:p299-309.

[101] Trichopoulos D. Epidemiologic studies of cancer and extremely low-frequency electric and magnetic field exposures. In: Health Effects of Low-Frequency Electric and Magnetic Fields. Report to the Committee on Interagency Radiation Research and Policy Coordination; Oak Ridge

[102] Savitz and Loomis observed a strong exposure-response relationship for brain tumors.[103] Several other researchers have found an increased risk of brain tumours linked to EMFs as a suspected agent.[104 105 106 107 108 109 110]

---

Associated Universities Panel. NTIS Publication #029- 000-00443-9: V-1-58. 1992.
[102] Savitz D A, Pearle N E, Poole C. Methodological issues in the epidemiology of electromagnetic fields and cancer. *Epidemiol Rev.* 1989; 11:p59-78.
[103] Savitz D A, Loomis D P. Magnetic field exposure in relation to leukemia and brain cancer mortality among electric utility workers. *Am J Epidemiol.* 1995; 141:p123-124.
[104] Kheifets L I, Afifi A A, Buffler P A, Zhang Z W. Occupational electric and magnetic field exposure and brain cancer: a meta analysis. *J Occup Environ Med.* 1996; 38(7):p655-658.
[105] Sorahan T, Nichols L, van Tongeren M, Harrington J M. Occupational exposure to magnetic fields relative to mortality from brain tumours: updated and revised findings from a study of United Kingdom electricity generation and transmission workers. *Occupational Environmental Medicine.* 2001; 58:p626-630.
[106] Guenel P, Nicolau J, Imberon E, Chevalier A, Goldberg M. Exposure to electric filed and incidence of leukemia, brain tumors, and other cancers among French electric utility workers. *Am J Epidemiol.* 1996; 144(12):p1107-1121.
[107] Kheifets L I. Electric and magnetic field exposure and brain cancer: A review. *Bioelectromagnetics.* 2001; Suppl 5:pS120-131.
[108] Schlehofer B, Kunze S W, Blettner M, Niehoff D, Wahrendorf J. occupatrional risk factors for brain tumors: results from a population-based case-control study in Germany. *Cancer Causes Control.* 1990; 1(3):p209-215.
[109] Villeneuve P J, Agnew D A, Johnson K C, Mao Y, Canadaian Cancer Registries Epidemiology Group. Brain cancer and occupational exposure to magnetic fields among

There has been an increasing amount of associated evidence linking the residential exposure from electromagnetic fields to both leukemia and childhood leukemia.[111] [112] [113] [114] [115]

Many of the investigators have found a definite association between miscarriage (spontaneous abortion) and magnetic fields.[116] [117]

men: results from a Canadian population-based case control study. *Int J Epidemiol.* 2002; 31:p210-217.

[110] Wei M, Guizzetti M, Yost M, Costa L G. Exposure to 60-Hz magnetic fields and proliferation of human astrocytoma cells in vitro. *Toxicology and Applied Pharmacology.* 2000; 162:p166-176.

[111] Feychting M, Ahlbom A. Childhood leukemia and residential exposure to weak extremely low frequency magnetic fields. Environ Health Perspect. 1995; 103 Suppl 2:p59-62.

[112] Miller M A, Murphy J R, Miller T I, et al. Variation in cancer risk estimates for exposure to powerline frequency electromagnetic fields: A meta-analysis comparing EMF measurement methods. *Risk Analysis.* 1995; 15:p281-287.

[113] Coleman M P, Bell C M J, Taylor H, et al. Leukemia and residence near electricity transmission equipment: A case control study. *Br J Cancer.* 1989; 60:p793-798.

[114] Linet M S, Hatch E E, Kleinerman R A, Robison L L, Kaune W T, Friedman D R, Severson R K, Haines C M, Hartsock C T, Niwa S, Wacholder S, Tarone R E. Residential exposure to magnetic fields and acute lymphoblastic leukemia in children. *N Engl J Med.* 1997; 337:p1-7.

[115] Feychting M, Ahlbom A. Magnetic fields, leukemia, and central nervous system tumors in Swedish adults residing near high-voltage lines. *Epidemiology.* 1994; 5:p501-509.

[116] Shaw G M, Croen L A. Human adverse reproductive outcomes and electromagnetic field exposures: review of epidemiological studies. *Environ Health Perspect.* 1993; 101(Suppl 4):p107-119.

Whether this is deemed to be spontaneous abortion, miscarriage or early pregnancy loss, too many researchers have found results to dismiss this finding. [118] Correlations as to the cause of miscarriage have been drawn from computers,[119][120] [121][122] electric blankets,[123][124] and EMFs from various sources.[125][126][127][128]

---

[117] Wertheimer N, Leeper E. Fetal loss associated with two seasonal sources of electromagnetic field exposure. *Am J Epidemiol.* 1989; 129:p220-224.
[118] Juutilainen J, Matilainen P, Saarikoski S, Laara E, Suonio S. Early preganancy loss and exposure to 50Hz magnetic fields. *Bioelectromagnetics.* 1992; 14:p229-236.
[119] McDonald A D, Cherry N M, Delorme C, McDonald J C. Visual display units and pregnancy: evidence from the Montreal survey. *J of Occup Med.* 1986; 28:p1226-1231.
[120]Goldhaber M K, Polen M, Hiat R. Miscarriages of women using computers in the workplace. *Amer J Industrial Med.* 1988; 13:p695.
[121] Schnorr T M, Grajewski Hornung R W, Thun M J, Egeland G M, Murray W E, Conover D L, Halperin W E. Video display terminals and the risk of spontaneous abortion. *N Engl J Med.* 1991; 324:p727-733.
[122] Lindbohm M L, Hietanen M, Kyyronen P, Sallmen M, Von Nandelstadh P, Taskinen H, Pekkarinen M, Ylikoski M, Hemminki K. Magnetic fields of video display terminals and spontaneous abortion. *Am J Epidemiol.* 1992; 136:p1041-1051.
[123] Belanger K, Leaderer B, Kellenbrand K, Holford T, et al. Spontaneous abortion and exposure to electric blankets and heated water beds. *Epidemiology.* 1998; 9:p36-42
[124] Wertheimer N, Leeper E. Possible effects of electric blankets and heated waterbeds on fetal development. *Bioelectromagnetics.* 1986; 7;p13-22.
[125] Hocking B, Joyner K. Re: Miscarriages among female physical therapists who report using radio- and microwave frequency electromagnetic radiation. A letter to the Editor. Am J Epidemiol. 1995; 141(3):p273-274.

Dr. De-Kun Li, an epidemiologist at the Kaiser Institute in Oakland, conducted a study in which approximately one thousand women in the first trimester of pregnancy wore a magnetic field meter around their waists for a day. He concluded that women exposed to an intermittent sixteen milliGauss (16 mG) electromagnetic field had a one hundred and eighty percent (180%) increased risk for spontaneous abortion.[129] Furthermore, the higher risks were found for women at less than ten weeks (220%) and women who had previously miscarried (310%).

Dr. Neil Cherry (2000) summarizes the general consensual findings, "Animal studies show that chromosome aberrations and single and double strand DNA breakage occurs with EMR (electromagnetic radiation) exposure; mice and rats have pregnancy, birth and fertility problems

---

[126] Ouellet-Hellstrom R, Stewart W F. Miscarriages among female physical therapists who report using radio- and microwave-frequency electromagnetic radiation. *Am J Epidemiol.* 1993; 138(10):p775-786.

[127] Larsen A I, Olsen J, Svane O. Gender specific reproductive outcome and exposure to high frequency electromagnetic radiation among physiotherapists. *Scand J Work Environ Health.* 1991; 17: p324-329.

[128] Taskinen H, Kyyronen P, Hemminki K. Effects of ultrasound, shortwaves, and physical exertion on pregnancy outcome in physiotherapists. *J of Epidemiology and Community Health.* 1990; 44:p196-210.

[129] Li D K, Odouli R, Wi S, et al. A population-based prospective cohort study of personal exposure to magnetic fields during pregnancy and the risk of miscarriage. 2002; *Epidemiology.* 13:p9-20.

associated with EMR exposure which are also found in exposed human populations. There is consistency within human studies and between human studies and animal studies."[130] "Electromagnetic fields and radiation, damage DNA and enhance cell death rates and therefore they are a Ubiquitos Universal Genotoxic Carcinogen that enhances the rates of Cancer, Cardiac, Reproductive and Neurological disease and mortality in human populations. Therefore there is no safe threshold level. The only safe exposure level is zero, a position confirmed by dose-response trends in epidemiological studies."

In 1983 the work of Dr. A. S. Davydov, of the Ukranian Academy of Sciences, was released, indicating that cellular chemistry in the brain could be affected by extremely low frequency radiation which he found could cross the blood brain barrier. According to the Defense & Foreign Affairs Daily, June 7, 1983, the Soviets have been conducting research on RF radiation since 1960. The purpose of this book is not to put forth the potential use of electromagnetic radiation as a weapon as espoused by the Citizens Against Human Rights Abuse,[131] but one should find it enlightening to understand the

---

[130] Cherry N. Critcism of the health assessment in the ICNIRP guidelines for radiofrequency and microwave radiation (100 kHz-300GHz). Lincoln University. 2000; p87.
[131] Welsh C. Electromagnetic Radiation (emr) Weapons: As Powerful As The Atomic Bomb. Citizens Against Humans Rights Abuse. Davis, CA. Feb. 2001.

full scope and potential damage that EMFs can inflict.

The impact of EMFs being able to affect neurological tissues such as the brain, makes the findings of the researchers, who have found neurodegenerative disorders such as decreased cognitive functions and Alzheimer's Disease, fall into the realm of not only being plausible, but totally credible as well. The question of the relationship between EMFs and neurological degeneration and cognitive function has been examined by many researchers. Many of them have found such a relationship.[132] [133]

Alzheimer's Disease (AD) is a progressive, irreversible, brain disorder with no known cause or cure, affecting more than four and a half million Americans. Unfortunately this disease leads to a rapid functional decline. The clinical cause of Alzheimer's disease is related to amyloid peptide microtubule deposits (tau), neurofibril entanglement and inflammation (neuronal toxicity).[134]

In 1994, Dr. Eugene Sobel, USC School of Medicine, and colleagues found an association

[132] Savitz D, Checkoway H, Loomis D. Magnetic field exposure and neurodegenerative disease mortality among electric utility workers. *Epidemiology.* 1998; 9:p398-404.
[133] Savitz D, Loomis D, Tse C K. Electrical occupations and neurodegenerative disease: Analyisis of U.S. mortality data. *Archives of Environmental Health.* 1998; 53:p1-5.
[134] Zlokovic B V, Deane R, Sallstromm J, Chow N, Miano J M. Neurovascular pathways and Alzheimer amyloid beta peptide. *Brain Pathol.* 2005; 15:p78-83.

between occupational exposure to EMFs and Alzheimer's disease. Sobel's team found that subjects who were occupationally exposed to "high" and "medium" levels of EMFs had a risk of developing Alzheimer's that was three times (300%) greater than those exposed to "low" levels of EMFs.[135] One potential mechanism was discovered by another of Dr. Sobel's investigations, where he found that people who are exposed to high EMFs occupationally, such as seamstresses, have three to five times the normal risk of contracting Alzheimer's disease due to deposits of the amyloid peptide protein.[136]

Some researchers look for factors that create increased risk while other look for those that create decreased risk. This was the case for a Turkish research group. Harmanci et al. (2003) studied the risk factors for Alzheimer's disease and came up with some particularly interesting findings. The research subjects with college or university degrees had a ninety percent (90%) decreased risk of AD. People who had electric heating in their homes had a two-hundred and seventy-seven percent (277%) increased risk for Alzheimer's disease and people

[135] Sobel E, Davanipour Z, Sulkava R, Erkinjuntti T, Wikstrom J, Henderson V W, Buckwalter G, Bowman J D, Lee P-J. Occupations with exposure to electromagnetic fields: A possible risk factor for Alzheimer's disease. *Am J Epidemiol.* 1995;142:p.515-524.
[136] Sobel E, Davanipour Z. Electromagnetic field exposure may cause increased production of amyloid beta and may eventually lead to Alzheimer's disease. *Neurology.* 1996;47:p.1594-1600.

who were exposed to the EMFs occupationally had a four hundred and two percent (402%) increased risk for being affected by this neurodegenerative disorder.[137]

Strickland (1996) and other investigators have found relationships between occupations and an increased incidence of ALS,[138] [139] some of which were found to involve consistently elevated EMFs (welding, soldering, electrical utility).[140] [141] Schulte et al. (1996) studied the incidence of neurodegenerative disorders and found that three of these diseases, Alzheimer's, Parkinson's and motor neuron disease (Amyotrophic lateral sclerosis) had increased incidence in occupations involving

---

[137] Harmanci H, Emre M, Gurvit H, Bilgic B, Hanagasi H, Gurol E, Sahin H, Tinaz S. Risk factors for Alzheimer disease: a population-based case-control study in Istanbul, Turkey. *Alzheimer Dis Assoc Disord.* 2003; 17(3):p139-145.

[138] Strickland D, Smith S A, Dolliff G, Goldman L, Roelofs R I. Amyotrophic lateral sclerosis and occupational history. A pilot case-control study. *Archives of Neurology.* 1996; 53:p730-733.

[139] Gunnarsson L G, Lindberg G, Soderfeldt B, Axelson O. Amyotrophic lateral sclerosis in Sweden in relation to occupation. *Acta Neurologica Scadinavica.* 1991; 83:p394-39.

[140] Davanipour Z, Sobel E,Bowman J D, Qian Z, Will A D. Amyotrophic lateral sclerosis and occupational exposure to electromagneric fields. *Bioelectromagnetics* 1997; *Bioelectromagnetics.* 1997; 18:p18-28.

[141] Johansen C, Olsen J H. Mortality from amyotrophic lateral sclerosis, other chronic disorders and electric shocks among utility workers. *Am J Epidemiol..* 1998; 148:p362-368.

pesticides, solvents, and electromagnetic fields.[142] Ahlbom (2001), after a review of the relationship between neurodegenerative diseases and electromagnetic fields, concluded that there is "relatively strong data indicating that electric utility work may be associated with an increased risk for amyotrophic lateral sclerosis."[143] Hakansson et al (2003) examined the relationship between extremely low frequency magnetic fields from occupational exposure and the mortality from neurodegenerative diseases. The conclusions support previous researchers' findings, demonstrating an increased risk of AD and ALS among employees occupationally exposed to EMFs.[144]

"Nine out of the ten epidemiological studies that have been conducted on the risk of ALS in relation to occupational exposure to EMF show moderate to strong relative risk estimates that supported a link between them.

---

[142] Schulte P A, Burnett C A, Boeniger M F, Johnson J. Neurodegenrative diseases: occupational occurrence and potential risk factors. *Am J Public Health.* 1996; 86:p1281-1288.
[143] Ahlbom A. Neurodegenarative diseases, suicide and depressive symptoms in relation to EMF. *Bioelectromagnetics.* 2001; Suppl 5:pS132-43.
[144] Hakansson N, Gustavsson P, Johansen C, Floderus B. Neurodegenerative diseases in welders and other workers exposed to high levels of magnetic fields. *Epidemiology.* 2003; 14:p420-426.

In case studies by Professor Magda Havas and David Stetzer, an EMF sensitive student's classroom behavior was positively affected by the removal of EMF radiation.[145] Several studies have linked decreased cognitive function,[146] dementia, depression,[147 148 149 150] and Alzheimer's Disease to increased exposure to EMFs.[151]

Childhood cancer concerns and the relationship to electromagnetic radiation have been an issue for more than twenty-five years. One of

[145]Havas M, Stetzer D. Dirty Electricity and Electrical Hypersensitivity: Five Case Studies. World Health Organization Workshop on Electrical Hypersensitivity, 25-26 October, Prague. 2004.

[146] Lyskov E, Juutilainen V, Jousmaki V, Hanninen O, et al. Influence of short-term exposure of magnetic field on the bioelectric processes of the brain and performance. *Int J Psychophysiol.* 1993; 14:p227-231

[147] Verkasalo P K, Kaprio J, Varjonen J, Romanov K, Heikkila K, Koskenvuo M. Magnetic fields of transmission lines and depression. *Am J Epidemiol.* 1997; 146(12);p1037-1045.

[148] Poole C, Kavet R, Funch D P, et al. Depressive symptoms and headaches in relation to proximity of residence to an alternating-current transmission line right-of-way. *Am J Epidemiol.* 1003; 137:p318-330.

[149] Perry S, Pearl L, Binns R. Power frequency magnetic field: depressive illness and myocardial infarction. *Public Health.* 1989; 103:p177-180.

[150] Beale I L, Pearce N E, Conroy D M, Henning M A, Murrell K A. Psychological effects of chronic exposure to 50 Hz magnetic fields in humans living near extra high voltage transmission lines. *Bioelectromagnetics.* 1997; 18:p584-594.

[151] Sobel E, Davanipour Z. Electromagnetic field exposure may cause increased production of amyloid beta and may eventually lead to Alzheimers disease. Neurology. 1996; 47:1591600.

the first published studies into EMF affects was the research out of the University of Colorado which noted a 200% to 300% increase in the cancer deaths of children living near power transmission lines in Denver, Colorado.[152] A point of interest in a Danish study found that children living near power lines emitting a 4 mG EMF had a five hundred percent (500%) increase in lymphomas, brain tumors and childhood leukemia.[153]

Dr. Antonio Sastre of the Midwest Research Institute observed that EMFs caused changes in heart rhythms (endogenous electrical impulses) that have been linked to increased risks of heart disease.[154] His conclusions led him to forecast that utility workers would have a higher rate of two types of cardiovascular disease. An epidemiological study corroborated Sastre's prediction that workers with high EMF exposure could show increased cardiovascular risk from arrhythmia and myocardial infarctions (heart attacks).[155]

---

[152] Wertheimer N, Leeper E. Electrical wiring configurations and childhood cancer. *Am J Epidemiol.* 1979; 109:p273-284.
[153] Olsen J H, Nielsen A, Schulgen G. Residence near high voltage facilities and risk of cancer in children. British Medical Journal. 1993; 307:p891-895.
[154]Sastre A, Cook M R, Graham C. Nocturnal exposure to intermittent 60 Hz magnetic fields alter human cardiac rhythm. *Bioelectromagnetics.* 1998; 19:p98-106.
[155] Savitz D A, Liao D, Sastre A, Kleckner R C. Magnetic field exposure and cardiovascular disease mortality among electric utility workers. *Am J Epidemiol.* 1999; 149:p135-142.

Hypertension, commonly known as high blood pressure, affects a broad segment of the population. The effects of EMFs on raising blood pressure, pulse rate and affecting other dynamics of cardiovascular function have been well documented.[156 157 158 159 160]

Cortisol decreases the effectiveness of the immune system by affecting leukocytes, eosinophils, neutrophils, phagocytes and T-lymphocytes.[161] These components are integral to defending the body against invading

---

[156] Braune S, Wrocklage C, Raczek J, Gailus T, Lucking C H. Resting blood pressure increased during exposure to a radio-frequency electromagnetic field. *Lancet.* 1998; 351:p1857-1858.

[157] Braune S, Reidel A, Schulte-Monting J, Raczek, J. Influence of a radio-frequency magnetic field on cardiovascular and hormonal parameters of the autonomic nervous system in healthy individuals. *Radiat Res.* 2002; 158:p352-356.

[158] Sait M L, Wood A W, Sadafi H A. A study of heart rate and heart rate variability in human subjects exposed to occupational levels of 50 Hz circular polarized magnetic fields. *Med Eng Phys.* 1999; 21(5):p361-369.

[159] Huber R, Schudererm J, Grat T, Jutz K, Borbely A A, Kuster N, Achermann P. Radio frequency electromagnetic field in humans: Estimation of SAR distribution in the brain, effects on sleep and heart rate. *Bioelectromagnetics.* 2003; 24:p262-276.

[160] Sastre A M, Cook R, Graham C. Nocturnal exposure to intermittent 60 Hz magnetic fields alters human cardiac rhythm. *Bioelectromagnetics.* 1998; 19:p98-106.

[161] Lyle D B, Ayotte R D, Sheppard A R, Adey W R. Suppression of t-lymphocyte cytotoxicity following exposure to 60-Hz sinusoidal electric fields. *Bioelectromagnetics.* 1988; 9(3):p303-313.

microorganisms and internal threats. As an example, investigators studying the ability of T-lymphocytes to destroy lymphoma cells found that a 450MHz magnetic field was able to inhibit the lymphocyte activity.[162]

Higher and more sustained serum cortisol levels, (such as those found in chronic stress or similar conditions) have been shown to have negative effects, such as decreased cognitive function, thyroid function, immune function, bone density and muscle tissue. Furthermore this increased serum cortisol also leads to hyperglycemia, hypertension and increased abdominal fat. EMFs cause increased serum cortisol.[163] [164]

Research has indicated that chronic exposure to EMFs can affect the adrenal, pituitary and pineal gland function.[165] [166] Serotonin

[162] Lyle D B, Schecter P, Adey W R, Lundak R L. Suppression of t-lymphocyte cytotoxicity following exposure to sinusoidally amplitude-modulated fields. *Bioelectromagnetics.* 1983; 4:p281-292.

[163] Hillman D. Exposure to electric and magnetic fields (EMF) linked to neuro-endocrine stress syndrome: increased cardiovascular disease, diabetes and cancer. *Shocking News.* 2005; (8):p2.

[164] Becker R O. Cross Currents: The Perils of Electropollution- the Promise of Electromedicine. Putnam Publishers. New York. 1990.

[165] Kavet R, Zaffanella L E, Daigle J P, Ebi K L. The possible role of contact of contact current in cancer risk associated with residential magnetic fields. *Bioeletromagnetics.* 2000; 21:p538-553.

production and serotonin receptors can be affected by EMFs.[167]

Cortisol increases serum glucose levels.[168] As a result of cortisol's influence on liver glycogen more glucose is released into the bloodstream. In other words, cortisol acts to inhibit the effects of insulin, predisposing an individual to diabetic serum glucose values. Insulin secretion by the pancreatic islets was decreased by exposure to EMFs, increasing serum glucose levels,[169] and also reduced its effectiveness to bind to its receptor.[170]

Increased serum cortisol can also cause mood swings, depression, insomnia, decrease memory and memory functions.[171]

---

[166] Kavet R. Review: Contact current hypothesis: Summary of results to date. *Bioelectromagnetics Supplement.* 2005; 7:pS75-S85.

[167] Sieron A, Labus L, Nowak P, Cieslar G, Brus H, Durczok A, Zagzit T, Kostrzewa T, Brus R. Alternating extremely low frequency magnetic field increases turnover of dopamine and serotonin in rat frontal cortex. *Bioelectromagnetics.* 2004; 25:p426-430.

[168] Berne R M, Levy M N, Koeppen B M, Stanton B A. Physiology. Fifth Edition. Mosby. Philadelphia. 1998.

[169] Sakurai T, Sataka A, Sumi S, Inoue K, Miyakoshi J. An extremely low magnetic field attenuates insulin secretion from the insulinoma cell line, RIN-m. *Bioelectromagnetics.* 2004; 25:p160-166.

[170] Li L, Dai Y, Xia R, Chen S, Qiao D. Pulsed electric field exposure of insulin induces anti-prolifeative effects on human hepatocytes. *Bioelectromagnetics.* 2005; 26:p1-9.

[171] Hillman D. Exposure to electric and magnetic fields (EMF) linked to neuro-endocrine stress syndrome: increased

Another proposed mechanism for EMF exposures increasing the risk of cancer was given credibility in a recent study by Juutilainen (2006). This recent paper demonstrated that in vitro and animal experiments show that EMFs increase the effects of known carcinogens.[172]

From the philosophical perspective, we know that there is no way we can rip out all of the electrical generating stations, transmission lines, and appliances, so we must deal with another aspect of the question: What can be done?

Suppression of the secretion of melatonin by the pineal gland has been suggested as a pathway for EMF effects on health. Henshaw and Reiter (2005) propose "that the melatonin hypothesis, in which power frequency magnetic fields suppress the nocturnal production of melatonin in the pineal gland, accounts for the observed increased risk of childhood leukemia."[173] The pineal gland is an endocrine organ located in the brain that secretes the hormone melatonin, which appears to play a

---

cardiovascular disease, diabetes and cancer. *Shocking News.* 2005; (8):p4.

[172] Juutilainen J, Kumlin T, Naarala J. Do extremely low frequency magnetic fields enhance the effects of environmental carcinogens? *Int J Radiat Biol.* 2006; 82(1):p1-12.

[173] Henshaw D L, Reiter R J. Do magnetic fields cause increased risk of childhood leukemia via melatonin disruption? *Bioelectromagnetics.* 2005; Suppl 7:pS86-97.

major role in sexual development, metabolism,[174] antioxidant functions,[175] and many other physiological activities.

Serum melatonin is reputed to be responsible for antioxidant, immunological and anti-tumor functions.[176] [177] [178] [179] [180] The evidence is absolutely overwhelming that the EMFs affect

[174] Axelrod J. The pineal gland.. *Endeavour.* 1970; 29 (108): p144-148.

[175] Pappola M A, Chyan Y J, Poeggeler B, Frangione B, Wilson G, Ghiso J, Reiter R J. An assessment of the antioxidant and the antimyloidogenic properties of melatonin: implications for Alzheimer's disease. *J Neural Transm.* 2000; 107:p203-231.

[176] Hillman D. Exposure to electric and magnetic fields (EMF) linked to neuro-endocrine stress syndrome: increased cardiovascular disease, diabetes and cancer. *Shocking News.* 2005; (8):p5.

[177] Badr F M, El Habit O H M, Harraz M M. Radioprotective effect of melatonin assessed by measuring chromosomal damage in mitotic and meiotic cells. *Mutation Research.* 1999; 444:p367-372.

[178] Vijayalaxmi, Reiter R J, Sewerynek E, Poeggeler B, Leal B Z, Meltz M L. Marked reduction of radiation-induced micronuclei in human blood lymphocytes pretreated with melatonin. *Radiation Research.* 1995; 143:p102-106.

[179] Vijayalaxmi, Reiter R J, Herman T S, Meltz M L. Melatonin and radioprotection from genetic damage: In vivo/in vitro studies with human volunteers. *Mutation Research.* 1996; 371:p221-228.

[180] Vijayalaxmi, Thomas C R Jr, Reiter R J, Herman T S. Melatonin: From basic research to cancer treatment clinics. *J Clin Oncology.* 2002; 20(10):p 2575-2601

serum melatonin and pineal gland function.[181] [182] [183] [184] [185]

Researchers have demonstrated that electric fields and ELFs (extremely low-frequency magnetic fields) as well as static magnetic fields depress melatonin secretion.[186] [187] [188] [189] [190] [191] [192] [193] [194] [195]

---

[181] Wilson B W, Anderson L E, Hilton D I, Phillips R D. Chronic exposure to 60-Hz electric fields: Effects on pineal function in the rat. *Bioelectromagnetics*. 1981; 2:p371-380.

[182] Grota L J, Reiter R J, Keng P, Michaelson S. Electric field exposure alters serum melatonin but not pineal melatonin synthesis in male rats. *Bioelectromagnetics*. 1994; 15:p427-437.

[183] Reiter R J, Anderson L E, Buschbom R L, Wilson B W. Reduction of the nocturnal rise in pineal melatonin levels in rats exposed to 60-Hz electric fields in utero and for 23 days after birth. *Life Science*. 1988; 42:p2203-2206.

[184] Wilson B W, Chess E K, Anderson L E. 60-Hz electric-field effects on pineal melatonin rhythms: Time course for onset and recovery. *Bioelectromagnetics*. 1986; 7:p239-242.

[185] Yellon SM. Acute 60 Hz magnetic field exposure effects on the melatonin rhythm in the pineal gland and circulation of the adult Djungarian hamster. *Journal of Pineal Research*. 1994; 16:p136-144.

[186] Wilson B W, Stevens R G, Anderson L E, eds. Extremely Low Frequency Electromagnetic Fields: The Question of Cancer. Columbus, OH (USA): Battelle Press, 1990.

[187] Brady J V, Reiter R J. Neurobehavioral effects. In: Health Effects of Low-Frequency Electric and Magnetic Fields. Report to the Committee on Interagency Radiation Research and Policy Coordination; Oak Ridge Associated Universities Panel. NTIS Publication #029-000-00443-9: VII-1-VII-56. 1992.

[188] Stevens R G. Re: Risk of postmenopausal breast cancer and use of electric blankets. *Am J Epi* 1995; 142:p146.

[189] Burch J B, Reif J S, Noonan C W, Yost M G. Melatonin metabolite levels in workers exposed to 60 Hz magnetic fields:

Melatonin plays a large role in human physiology aside from regulating normal rhythms. Dr. Russell Reiter suggests that the suppression of melatonin by magnetic fields could result in a higher incidence of

---

work in substations and with 3-phase conductors. *J Occup Envir Med.* 2000; 42:p136-142.

[190] Arnetz B B, Berg M. Melatonin and adrenocorticotropic hormone levels in video display unit workers during work and leisure. *J Occup Med.* 1996; 38(11):p1108-1110.

[191] Selmaoui B, Touitou Y. Sinusoidal 50-Hz magnetic fields depress rat pineal NAT activity and serum melatonin. Role of duration and intensity of exposure. *Life Science.* 1995; 57:p1351-1358.

[192] Kato M, Honma K, Shigemitsu T, Shiga Y. Effects of exposure to a circularly polarized 50-Hz magnetic field on plasma and pineal melatonin levels in rats. *Bioelectromagnetics.* 1993; 14:p97-110.

[193] Truong H, Yellon S M. Effect of various acute 60 Hz magnetic field exposures on the nocturnal melatonin rise in the adult Djungarian hamster. *Journal of Pineal Research.* 1997; 22:p177-183.

[194] Kato M, Honma K, Shigemitsu T, Shiga Y. Circularly polarized 50-Hz magnetic field exposure reduces pineal gland melatonin and blood concentrations of long-evans rats. *Neuroscience Letters.* 1994; 166:p59-62.

[195] Wilson B W, Wright C w, Morris J F, Buschbom R L, Brown D P, Miller D L, Sommers-Flannigan R, Anderson L E. Evidence for an effect of elf electromagnetic fields on human pineal gland function. *Journal of Pineal Research.* 1990; 9:p259-269.

cancer in any tissue,[196] and certainly predispose one to neurodegenerative disorders and dementia.[197]

The work of Dr. Eva Schernhammer not only corroborates the melatonin theory but suggests that other cancers, aside from breast cancer, such as colorectal cancer may be related to decreased serum melatonin.[198] [199] Colorectal cancer is one of the most common forms of cancer and occurs approximately once in every five cases. The fact that EMFs can affect a broad range of hormonal secretions[200] may in fact be the solution to one of

---

[196] Rogers W R, Reiter R J, Smith H D, Barlow-Walden L. Rapid-onset/offset, variably scheduled 60 Hz electric and magnetic field exposure reduces nocturnal serum melatonin concentration in nonhuman primates. *Bioelectromagnetics.* 1995; S3:119-122.

[197] Reiter R J, Tan D X, Pappolla M A. Melatonin relieves the neural oxidative burden that contributes to dementias. *Ann N Y Acad Sci.* 2004; 1035:p179-196.

[198] Schernhammer E S, Hankinson S E. Urinary melatonin levels and breast cancer risk. *J Natl Cancer Inst.* 2005; 97(14):p1084-1087.

[199] Schernhammer E S, Laden F, Speizer F E, Willett W C, Hunter D J, Kawachi I, Fuchs C S, Colditz G A: Night-shift work and risk of colorectal cancer in the Nurses' Health Study. *J Natl Cancer Inst.* 2003; 95(11): p825-828.

[200] Davis S, Mirick D K, Chen C, Stanczyk F Z. Effects of 60-Hz magnetic field exposure on nocturnal 6-Sulfatoxymelatonin, estrogens, luteinizing hormone, and follicle-stimulating hormone in healthy reproductive age women: Results of a crossover trials. *Ann Epidemiol* 2006; 16 (8): 622 - 631

the mysteries of the magnetic field/cancer diversity issue.[201]

There is a certain segment of the population that suffers from a condition known as electrical hypersensitivity. Although Hillert et al (2002) has found one to two percent (1%-2%) of the Swedish population to be electromagnetically hypersensitive,[202] current estimates reveal that approximately three percent (3%) of the population has this sensitivity and another thirty-five percent have some symptoms of EHS.[203] The rest of the population may or may not be aware of the effects of electromagnetic fields, but by no means does that indicate that they are unaffected.

Electromagnetic fields are produced by so many of our modern conveniences that most of us are unwilling to forgo them and cannot revert back to a simpler, perhaps somewhat less convenient lifestyle. There are currently almost four billion, cell phones in use on the planet and of course the millions of cell phone towers (masts) that allow these phones to function. That is more than one cell phone for more than one half of the population of

[201] Stevens R.G, Wilson B W, Anderson L E. The Melatonin Hypothesis: Breast cancer and the use of electric power. Columbus, Ohio: Battelle Press. 1997.

[202] Hillert L, Berglind N, Arnetz B B, Bellander T. Prevalence of self-reported hypersensitivity to electric magnetic fields in a population-based questionnaire survey. *Scand j Work Environ Health.* 2002; 28(1):p33-41.

[203] Philips A, Philips J. The Power Watch Handbook. Piatkus Books. London. 2006; p294.

earth. The real question we should be asking is how safe are they, because these devices totally fill our environment and then to top it off we hold them beside our largest collection of neurological tissue... our brain.

According to the late Dr. Neil Cherry, Professor of Environmental Health, Lincoln University, New Zealand, we should be reminded that EMFs are a "ubiquitous universal genotoxic carcinogen" where there is no minimum threshold and "the only safe exposure level is zero." One of the problems that we are all currently facing is the fact that there is virtually no place left on the planet where we can be free of the radio frequency wavelengths that now transmit information.

In 1998 Hocking published his findings related to the symptoms associated with analog and digital cellular phones. These symptoms included discomfort, dizziness, difficulty concentrating, memory loss, fatigue, headache, burning skin sensations (a sensation of warmth on or near the ear) and tingling and tightness of the skin near the phone.[204] In that same year, Dr. Kjell Mild examined eleven thousand (11,000) cell phone users and corroborated all of symptoms found by Hocking and stated that fatigue, headaches and

---

[204] Hocking B. Preliminary report: Symptoms associated with mobile phone use. *Occ Med.* 1998; 48(6):p.357-360.

burning sensations are more frequent symptoms of those people who make longer phone calls.[205]

Since those initial findings the association and dose-relationships between cell phones and disease place cell phone users into a high risk health group.[206] Cell phones can cause DNA damage, headaches, blurred vision, dizziness, fatigue, short term memory loss, neuralgias, tumors, and sleep disturbances to name a few.[207 208 209 210 211]

In the early 1990's, Lai and Singh developed a technique to determine genetic damage in

---

[205]Mild, K H., Oftedal, G, Sandstrom M., Wilen J, Tynes T, Haugsdal B, Hauger E. Comparison of symptoms by users of analogue and digital mobile phones - A Swedish-Norwegian epidemiological study. *National Institute for Working Life*, Umea, Sweden. 1998; 23: p.84.

[206] Gandhi G A, Singh P. Mobile phone users: Another high health risk group. *J Hum Ecol.* 2005; 18(2):p.85-92.

[207] Lai H, Singh N P. Acute low-intensity microwave exposure increases DNA single-strand breaks in rat brain cells. *Bioelectromagnetics.* 1995; 16:p.207-210.

[208] Hamblin D L, Wood A W. Effects of mobile phone emissions on human brain activity and sleep variables. *Int J Radiat Biol.* 2002; 78:p.659-669.

[209] Gandhi G A, Singh P. Mobile phone users: Another high health risk group. *J Hum Ecol.* 2005; 18(2):p.85-92.

[210]Ahlbom A, Green A, Kheifets L, Savitz D, Swerdlow A. Epidemiology of health effects of radiofrequency exposure. *Environ Health Perspect.* 2004; 112:p.1741-1754.

[211] Mild, K H., Oftedal, G, Sandstrom M., Wilen J, Tynes T, Haugsdal B, Hauger E. Comparison of symptoms by users of analogue and digital mobile phones - A Swedish-Norwegian epidemiological study. *National Institute for Working Life*, Umea, Sweden. 1998; 23: p.84.

peripheral blood lymphocytes called single cell gel electrophoresis. This technique was able to recognize DNA fragments that represented the appearance of a 'comet' under the scrutiny of a microscope. The increased length of the 'comet's' tail represented an increased degree of DNA damage.[212]

Aside from his numerous investigations into melatonin, Vijayalaxmi (1997) irradiated transgenic (predisposed to developing human tumours) mice to a continuous cell phone signal and found a forty-one percent (41%) increase in tumour growth and twelve and a half per cent (12.5%) increase in chromosome damage in bone and blood.[213]

Dr. Leif Salford and his group of Swedish researchers found that cell phone radiation at all levels cause significant blood brain barrier leakage.[214] [215] The blood brain barrier is a network

---

[212] Lai H, Singh H P. Single and double strand DNA breaks in rat brain cells after acute exposure to radiofrequency electromagnetic radiation *Int J Radiat Biol.* 1996; 69:p.513-521.

[213] Vijayalaxmi B Z, Frei M R, Dusch S J, Guel V, Meltz M L, Jauchem J R. Frequency of micronuclei in the peripheral blood and bone marrow of cancer-prone mice chronically exposed to 2450 MHz radiofrequency radiation. *Radiation Research.* 1997a; 147: p495-500.

[214] Salford L G, Brun A, Sturesson K, Eberhardt J L, Persson B R. Permeability of the blood-brain barrier induced by 915 MHz electromagnetic radiation, continuous wave and modulated at 8, 16, 50, and 200 Hz. Microsc Res Tech. 1994; 27(6):p.535-42.

of tightly packed endothelial cells that line the blood vessels that supply the brain. Their function is to keep toxins and potentially harmful chemicals from entering the highly sensitive neurological tissues of the brain, decreasing the chance of physiological malfunction. When the blood brain barrier is opened, the potential for cerebral disorders and disease of all kinds is increased.

Cell phones have also been shown to decrease cognitive function by increasing reaction time[216] and decreasing performance in memory testing.[217] [218] Keeping in perspective the ever-increasing number of people suffering from Alzheimer's disease (over four million in the U.S. today) and those diagnosed with some form of senility or cognitive dysfunction, does it not make

---

[215] Carlo G, Schram M. Cell Phones: Invisible Hazards in the Wireless Age. Carroll & Graf Publishers. New York. 2001; p.111.

[216] Hamblin D L, Wood A W, Croft R J, Stough C. Examining the effects of electromagnetic fields emitted by GSM mobile phones on human event-related potentials and performance during an auditory task. *Clin Neurophysiol.* 2004; 115:p.171-178.

[217] Krause C M, Harrala C, Sillanmäki L, Koivisto M, Alnko K, Reyonsuo A, Laine M, Hämäläinen H. Effects of electromagnetic field emitted by cellular phones on the EEG during an auditory memory task: a double blind replication study. *Bioelectromagnetics.* 2004; 25:p.33-40.

[218] Koivisto M, Revonsuo A, Krause C, Haarala C, Sillanmäki L, Laine M, Hämäläinen H. Effects of 902 MHz electromagnetic field emitted by cellular telephones on response times in humans. *Neuroreport.* 2000; 11(2):p.413-15.

sense to consider the possible effects from the pervasive microwave (cell phone) radiation as a potential factor in these cases. India has the fastest growing cell phone market in the world, adding eighty-three million subscribers in 2007 alone.[219] Dr. G. A. Gandhi, one of India's leading researcher into cell phone microwave radiation states, "Exposure to radio frequency (RF) signals generated by cell phones have increased dramatically and are reported to affect physiological, neurological, cognitive and behavioural changes and to induce, initiate and promote carcinogenesis."[220]

In a very recent paper (December 2007), new findings have offered warnings against cell phone use before sleep.[221] The study was carried out in both Sweden (Karolinska Institute) and the United States (Wayne State University) and is believed to have been the most comprehensive study carried out in this type of investigation.[222] The findings are a stern warning for children and

[219] Singh S. "With 83m additions in a year, India fastest growing cell mkt." *The Times Of India.* Saturday February 16, 2008;p.21.

[220] Gandhi G A. Genetic damage in mobile phone users: some preliminary findings. *Indian J Hum Genet.* 2005;11:p.99-104.

[221] Lean G. Mobile hone radiation wrecks your sleep. *The Independent.* January 20, 2008.

[222] Arnetz B B, Akerstedt T, Hillert L, Lowden A, Kuster N, Wiholm C. the Effectsof 884 Mhz GSM Wireless Communication Signals on Self=reported Symptom and Sleep.(EEG)=An Experimental Provocation Study. Piers Online. 2007; 3(7):p.1148-1150.

teenagers who use their phones late at night and, need sleep especially because of their growth phases. The lack of proper deep REM sleep has the potential to alter their moods and lead to "personality changes, ADHD-like symptoms, depression, lack of concentration and poor academic performance."

When we bear in mind the fact that so little is known about the bioaccumulation effects of EMFs or in fact what portion of these fields is capable of causing health issues, there might be an element to further investigate. The theoretical possibility of the existence of an accumulated electromagnetic field threshold, that predisposes any individual to a diseased state when surpassed, seems to validate the risk factor and incidence of disease that so many researchers have found as an associative or causal relationship with exposure.

One thing is certain and it is only common sense in light of so many experimental observations, "These (experimental) results highlight a correlation between mobile phone use (exposure to RFR) and genetic damage and require interim public health actions in the wake of widespread use of mobile telephony."[223] The BioInitiative Working Group has echoed these sentiments, "Toxicity to the genome can lead to a change in cellular functions, cancer and cell death. One can conclude that under certain conditions RF is genotoxic (cause genetic

---

[223] Gandhi G A. Genetic damage in mobile phone users: some preliminary findings. *Indian J Hum Genet.* 2005;11:p.99-104.

damage)."[224] "RF may be considered to be genotoxic."[225]

One of the most difficult problems that we face when discussing the effects of EMFs and RFs is the determination of the latency period or lag time between exposure to any potential carcinogen and the outbreak of the disease. Anti-aging specialist, Dr. Ira L Goodman, (M.D. FACS, ABHM, FAAAM), candidly expresses the latency period issue succinctly, "It can take years for EMFs (electromagnetic fields) to damage biological tissues and the endpoints are non specific."

Cell phones have not been in use for a long time (into the third decade) but the evidence points to the fact that there is a disease relationship to electromagnetic field exposure. A good example of this can be seen when discussing the nuclear meltdown at Chernobyl. When referring to the cases of thyroid cancer resulting from this tragedy, Dr Elaine Ron, from the US National Cancer Institute in Bethesda, Maryland, said: "The elevated risk of thyroid cancer appears to continue throughout life, but there is some indication that the risk may be highest 15 to 19 years after exposure." If we were to extrapolate the growing use of cell phones, increasing amounts of cell towers, and the

---

[224] Sage C, Carpenter D, Eds. BioInitiative Report: A Rationale for a Biologically-based Public Exposure Standard for Electromagnetic Fields (ELF and RF). BioInitiative Working Group. USA. August 31, 2007; Table 1-1.
[225] Ibid.

virtually omnipresent Wi-Fi signals with the known relationships to disease and the projected latency periods, it is safe to say that the worst is yet to come. Wi-Fi signals, like cell phone towers, are always radiating.

Perhaps the most concise expression of the cellular phone risk can be found in Dr. G. A. Gandhi's work after conducting her own experiments and reviewing the body of scientific work, "In the light of this literature it can be observed that the studies documenting positive genotoxicity are those where there is mostly in vivo occupational exposure to RFR of mobile phone range. The present study clearly demonstrates the same, albeit the exposure is directly through mobile phone use. There is a potential for a very large worldwide public health impact in the wake of the results of this study and calls for interim public health protective measures."[226]

There is some light on the horizon. Another invention of Dr. Smirnov also patented in the United States, the MRET-Shield polymer is able to generate random, low frequency electromagnetic waves that will superimpose themselves onto damaging electromagnetic radiation waves, compensating their adverse effect or even rendering them harmless to biological systems such as

---

[226] Gandhi G A. Genetic damage in mobile phone users: some preliminary findings. *Indian J Hum Genet.* 2005;11:p.99-104.

humans, animals and plants.[227] The MRET-Sheild device counts amongst the most major scientific breakthroughs of the century. Help is on the way.

---

[227]Smirnov I V. Polymer Material Providing Compatibility between Technologically Originated EMR and Biological Systems. *Explore Magazine*. 2006;15(4):p.26-32.

# CHAPTER 5

# THE DAWN OF
# PROTECTION

*"Like a flash of lightning and in an instant the truth was revealed. I drew with a stick on the sand the diagrams of my motor. A thousand secrets of nature which I might have stumbled upon accidentally I would have given for that one which I had wrestled from her against all odds and at the peril of my existence."*

**Nikola Tesla,
The inventor of AC current**

The threat is real. Whether nature was merely trying to save us from ourselves or perhaps it was just the serendipitous fate of Dr. Smirnov's findings mingled with his brilliance. Whatever it was, it is fortunate for us all that it did occur, and the timing could not have been better. From the preceding chapter and the hundreds of papers that draw the relationship between electromagnetic fields and the cellular dysfunction leading to numerous disease processes, the facts are undeniable. Much of the controversy regarding the existence of a cellular response to low-energy radiation is due both to the fact that the reproducibility of some experiments has proven difficult, and to the theoretical objections that the energy of such weak fields would be less than the energy of the background noise caused by the temperature at which the cells are studied (*thermal noise*). It should be noted, however, that the relationship has been established beyond the point that it can be dismissed.

We are constantly exposed to electromagnetic fields. There are more than three and a half billion cell phones in use in the world today, and rapidly approaching four billion. Looking down from a rooftop restaurant in the Indian city of Madurai, there are more cell towers than can be counted. Perhaps this is due to the five networks competing for the cellular business of the rapidly increasing Indian marketplace that in the next five years will probably have close to one billion cell phone users. Perhaps it is due to the fact that the richest people in the world own cellular (wireless) providers companies and that it is just good business to provide their service for a minimal fee. (You can now buy a cellular airtime package only a few dollars (U.S.) in India that will give you all incoming calls free for five years with no monthly maintenance fees.)

This is how the global expansion of this vast fiscal wireless empire is progressing. Sadly, little or no concern is being given to the negative effects of this radiation, meanwhile, the number of cell phones and cell phone towers increases daily. Some people think that because they do not carry a cell phone they are safe. Ask yourself this question: does your cell phone work indoors? Microwave radiation passes through everything between the cell tower to connect to every cell phone linked to the network. If any individual is standing between a cell tower and any cell phone on that network, the radiation will pass through every person that lies in the path. Nothing can block it and that is why your cell phone works indoors.

What can be done about it? There is no way to substantially block any form of electromagnetic radiation (EMR or EMF) or radio frequency radiation (RF) however there is a way to disguise it. It would be advantageous if there were a device available that could effectively shield people, animals and plants against the harmful, adverse health consequences that are inherent in the prolonged, extended or even minimal exposure to EMR.

Electromagnetic random (noise) fields have been shown to interfere with the reception of damaging radiation at the cellular level (protein receptors on the cellular membrane) offering a form of shielding and therefore no damage can ensue.[228]

---

[228] Li C, Jiang H, Fu Y. A study on dose-effect of suppression to gap junctional intercellular communication function by 50-Hz magnetic fields]
Zhonghua Yu Fang Yi Xue Za Zhi. 1998;32(3): p.142-4.
Chinese.

[229] [230] [231] [232] Controlled experiments have been conducted where the biological effects of damaging electromagnetic radiation was nullified by the superimposition of electromagnetic noise fields onto the radiation wave. [233]

This is precisely the application performed by the MRET-Shield polymer.[234] The United States patent for this EMR shielding material was issued to Dr. Smirnov in 2002 and since then the product has been recognized worldwide. External high frequency electromagnetic fields (EMRs) generate

---

[229] Zeng Q, Chiang H, Fu Y, Lu D, Xu Z. Electromagnetic noise blocks the gap-junctional intercellular communication suppression induced by 50 Hz magnetic field] Zhonghua Lao Dong Wei Sheng Zhi Ye Bing Za Zhi. 2002;20(4):p.243-5. Chinese

[230] Litovitz T A, Montrose C J, Doinov P, Brown K M, Barber M. Superimposing spatially coherent electromagnetic noise inhibits field-induced abnormalities in developing chick embryos. *Bioeletromagnetics.* 1994;15(2):p.105-13.

[231] Litovitz T A, Penafiel L M, Farrel J M, Krause D, Meister R, Mullins J M. Bioeffects induced by exposure to microwaves are mitigated by superposition of ELF noise. *Bioelectromagnetics.* 1997; 18(6):p.422-30.

[232]Litovitz T A, Krause D, Montrose C J, Mullins J M. Temporally incoherent magnetic fields mitigate the response of biological systems to temporally coherent magnetic fields. *Bioelectromagnetics.* 1994; 15(5):p.399-409.

[233] Zeng Q, Ke Z, Gao X, Fu, Y, Lu D, Chiang H, Xu, Z. Noise Magnetic Fields Abolish the Gap Junction Intercellular Communication Suppression Induced by 50 Hz Magnetic Fields. *Bioelectromagnetics.* 2006;27(4):p.274-9.

[234]Smirnov I V. (2005) Comparative Study of the Effect of Microwave Radiation Neutralizers on Physiological State of Human Subjects. *Explore Magazine.* 2005;(14)5: p.29-44.

an excitatory response in the crystalline piezoelectric structures of the MRET-Shield polymer compound. Subsequently, the MRET-Shield polymer generates biologically active subtle electromagnetic waves which are superimposed onto the initial high frequency electromagnetic radiation and can interact with biological systems, shielding the receptors from detection of RF radiation and transmitting the information that supports and improves cellular functions in the body.[235] In other words, the potentially damaging radiation becomes just another vibration that is meaningless and unable to harm the body.

There have been many experiments conducted that have demonstrated the ability of the MRET-Shield polymer to provide protection for human tissue. The intent of this book is to re-iterate the message that we are at risk from electromagnetic fields and to demonstrate the physiological benefits of the MRET-Shield polymer. Cell phones have been shown to cause abnormal results in a number of diagnostic tests and by reviewing these findings we can best demonstrate the effectiveness and protection ability of MRET-Shield polymer.

Since thermal noise (the creation of heat by wave generation) has demonstrated the ability to mask the propagation of the very subtle random

---

[235]Smirnov I V. Polymer Material Providing Compatibility between Technologically Originated EMR and Biological Systems. *Explore Magazine.* 2006;15(4):p.26-32.

noise field that is generated by the MRET-Shield polymer, we must use other methods to prove the beneficial abilities of the MRET-Shield polymer. To put it simply, if we cannot see the process happening, but we can see the results, we must show the results.

Fortunately there are many parameters that can be used to demonstrate both the potentially physiological disrupting effects caused by EMFs and the subsequent elimination of these effects by the MRET-Shield polymer. Well-known and accepted diagnostic criteria can be used. Studies such as electroencephalogram (EEG), vascular perfusion studies (blood flow) of the brain using magnetic resonance angiography, thermography, specific absorption rate (SAR), and live blood cell analysis adequately relate the beneficial findings using cell phone radiation as the stimulating electromagnetic field.

## LIVE BLOOD CELL ANALYSIS (DARKFIELD MICROSCOPY)

In the following figures, (Figures XXVII, XXVIII, XXVIX) a lancet was used to extract a drop of blood from the fingertip of the subject. This drop was placed on a microscopic slide using the darkfield microscopic technique. This procedure is significantly different from standard microscopy. With this technique, light does not travel directly through the specimen, but comes in from the sides and only the light which is reflected by the specimen is viewed against a dark background creating a highly contrasted image.[236]

The Live Blood Cell Analysis was conducted at the laboratory of Quantum Biotech in Singapore. The drops of blood used as samples were drawn from the subject both before and after his introduction to the EMR of the cell phone during five minutes with and without the installation of MRET-Shield. The blood samples were observed under the microscope. The actual experimental procedure was as follows: The initial drop of blood was drawn as a control. The subject talked on an unprotected cell phone for five minutes and another drop of blood was drawn. After twenty minutes another drop of blood was drawn to ensure that the effects of the cell phone had resided. The subject then talked on a MRET-Shield protected cell phone for five minutes and the final drop of blood was drawn.

As can be seen from the control image (Figure XXVII), the red blood cells (RBCs) appear non-clustered, with clearly defined margins. This is a good example of RBCs that will be able to circulate freely down even the smallest capillary and deliver the oxygen needed by all cells.

The same procedure was used for the next sample (Figure XXVIII), however the subject had

---

[236] Hayden J E. Adventures on the Dark Side: An Introduction to Darkfield Microscopy. *BioTechniques*. 2002; 32(4): p.756-761.

talked on an unprotected cellular phone for five minutes. Notice the derangement of the RBCs positioning and the consistent Rouleau (roll of coins) formation. The clustering will create problems for the delivery of oxygen to the tissues due to the fact that these red blood cells may not be able to travel down the smaller blood vessels.

Figure XXIX shows the microscopic slide of the live blood cell sample taken after the subject talked on a cell phone for five minutes with the MRET-Shield polymer cell phone chip in place near the antenna. One will note the lack of Rouleau and the clearly defined margins of the red blood cells. This orientation is virtually identical to the control sample taken from the same subject, indicating that

**FIGURE XXVII**
**LIVE BLOOD CELL ANALYSIS**
**CONTROL SAMPLE**

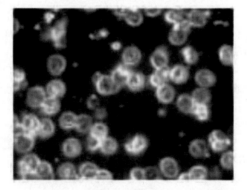

### FIGURE XXVIII
### LIVE BLOOD CELL ANALYSIS
### CELL PHONE

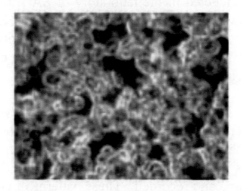

### FIGURE XXIX
### LIVE BLOOD CELL ANALYSIS MRET CHIP

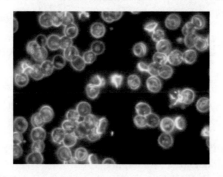

the electromagnetic radiation from the cell phone
with the MRET-Shield chip in place did not cause
the physiological damage evident in the previous
slide.

## ELECTROENCEPHALOGRAM STUDY

The electroencephalogram (EEG) testing was conducted in the laboratory of SA Biomedical Instrumentation in San Diego, California. EEG tests measure the pattern of electrical conductivity in the brain. Brain cells communicate with each other by producing electrical impulses.

In a standard EEG test, electrodes, which are connected to an amplifier, are placed on the scalp in a number of different locations. The electronic signals created by the brain are then detected, measured and recorded. These patterns of electrical activity can then be examined to determine normal or abnormal (pathological) brain wave function.[237] Abnormal EEG findings can indicate conditions such as epilepsy (seizures), head injuries, migraine headaches, sleep disorders, and attention deficit disorders (ADD) to name a few.[238] [239]

The following tests were conducted on a subject who had been exposed to the electromagnetic radiation generated by a cellular phone (SAMSUNG Model No: SCH-2000) located

---

[237] Epstein C M. *Introduction to EEG and evoked potentials.* J. B. Lippincot Co. Philadelphia. 1983.

[238] Sullivan F W, Gentile K, Boelhouwer C. Relationship of Clinical Symptomatology to Abnormal EEG Findings: A Family Study. *Am J Psychiatry.* 1967;124:p.554-559.

[239] Thatcher R W, North D, Biver C. EEG and intelligence: relations between EEG coherence, EEG phase delay and power. *Clin Neurophysiol.* 2005;116(9):p.2129-41.

in the usual operating position on the right side of the head. Three tests were conducted following the standard methodology. The head of a subject was covered with a standard Electro-cap E1-L connected with four channels SAI Bioelectric Amplifier which includes an Analog Processor and Anti-aliasing Filters.

## FIGURE XXX
## ELECTROENCEPHALOGRAM
## BASE LINE

**CONTROL EEG CHART OF SUBJECT
NOT INTRODUCED TO EMR OF CELLULAR PHONE**

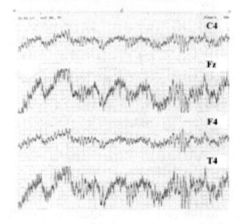

One of the tests was the baseline reading of brain wave activity. The subject demonstrated what is considered to be a normal slow mode EEG pattern for the control testing.

During the next two trials, the same cellular phone was located in standard operating position at the right side of a head of the same subject. The subject operated a cell phone in the standard position for three minutes.

### FIGURE XXXI
### ELECTROENCEPHALOGRAM
### ACTIVE CELL PHONE

**EEG** CHART OF SUBJECT INTRODUCED TO **EMR** OF CELLULAR PHONE WITHOUT ANY PROTECTION

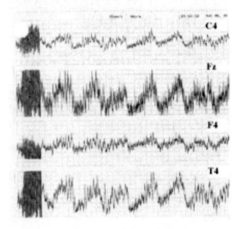

The EEG chart of the subject after his exposure to the cell phone radiation (Figure XXXI) demonstrates an excitatory state of brain wave activity and can be clearly seen to be abnormal and perhaps indicative of a potential problem.

The EEG pattern expressed in the next chart of the subject following his exposure to the radiation of the cell phone with the MRET-Shield

## FIGURE XXXII
## ELECTROENCEPHALOGRAM
## ACTIVE CELL PHONE WITH MRET-SHIELD

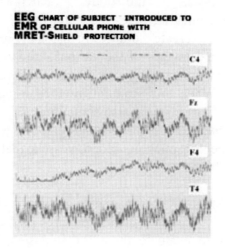

EEG CHART OF SUBJECT INTRODUCED TO EMR OF CELLULAR PHONE WITH MRET-SHIELD PROTECTION

installed (Figure XXXII) is considered to be a normal slow mode pattern.

The comparison of the EEG charts representing the brain wave patterns shows that the EEG chart of the subject introduced to the EMR with the MRET-Shield polymer protection is very close to the control EEG chart. The significance of this finding is that the electrical activity of the brain is unaffected by the electromagnetic radiation of the cell phone. This means that the installation of the MRET-Shield polymer is able to confer protection from the damaging effects of cellular phone radiation.

## MAGNETIC RESONANCE ANGIOGRAPHY

Magnetic Resonance Angiography is a diagnostic evaluation used to determine the status of blood vessels in the body MRI (magnetic resonance imaging) uses magnetic fields and radio waves to create multi-dimensional or three-dimensional images of the various structures inside your body, including the heart, brain or blood vessels. When this scanning method is applied to the blood vessels, it is also sometimes referred to as MRA (magnetic resonance angiography), which is a technique for imaging blood vessels that contain flowing blood.

Magnetic Resonance Angiography (MRA) is commonly used to generate pictures of the arteries in order to evaluate them for stenosis (abnormal narrowing) or aneurysms (arterial wall dilations which are at risk of rupturing). An MRA technique known as "flow-related enhancement" (e.g. three-dimensional real-time sequences) was used to acquire the images about to be presented. Using this technique, the majority of the signal that creates the image is due to the presence of blood which has recently moved into that plane.

The test results provide analysis for the following sections: Cerebrum, top view; Cross section of brain at the brain stem level; Arteries of brain, bottom view of brain; Left – Right hemisphere sequence function. The results were confirmed by the three dimensional MRA test which was conducted by Tex Chu Technology Corporation located in Taiwan. The test was conducted on a human subject who was exposed to cell phone radiation emitted by a Sony Ericsson T630 model phone. The test was conducted both with and without the installation of the MRET-Shield chip, and of course with no phone at all to determine a control value of cerebral vascular blood flow.

In this study, the computer has been instructed to review the magnetic resonance angiogram and mark areas based on blood flow in the brain (cerebral vascular perfusion). The printed images show the previously mentioned four different views of the brain. Regions displaying excellent to good blood flow have been marked with a white or yellow octagon. Regions with fair blood flow are marked with a red arrow pointing up. Areas of decreased or diminished blood flow are marked with a red diamond or an arrow pointing down or even a black mark.

Figure XXXIII revealing the subject's control values depicts a relatively good blood flow. The majority of the blood flow markings are the yellow octagons and red upward arrows with very few indications of poor blood flow, although there are some.

# FIGURE XXXIII
## MAGNETIC RESONANCE ANGIOGRAM
## CONTROL

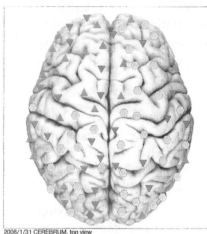

2006/1/31 CEREBRUM, top view

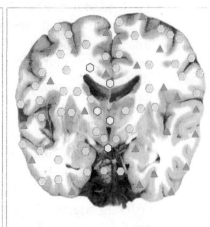

2006/1/31 CROSS SECTION OF BRAIN ; at the brain stem level

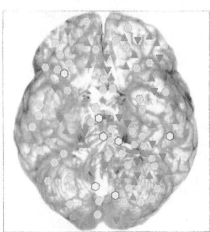

2006/1/31 ARTERIES OF BRAIN, view from below

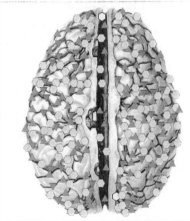

2006/1/31

## FIGURE XXXIV
## MAGNETIC RESONANCE ANGIOGRAM
## ACTIVE CELL PHONE

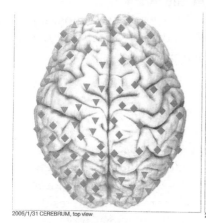

2006/1/31 CEREBRUM, top view

Sony Ericsson T630 型號手機無 EMRON 防護

2006/1/31 CROSS SECTION OF BRAIN ; at the brain stem level

Sony Ericsson T630 型號手機無 EMRON 防護

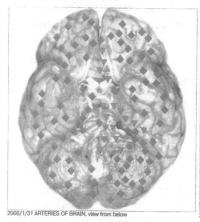

2006/1/31 ARTERIES OF BRAIN, view from below

Sony Ericsson T630 型號手機無 EMRON 防護

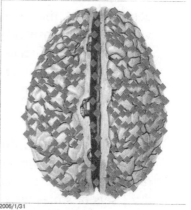

2006/1/31

Sony Ericsson T630 型號手機無 EMRON 防護

呂晉宏博士 適性適量細胞營養健康中心

The angiogram during the unprotected cell phone use (Figure XXXIV) shows a significant decrease of cerebral-vascular blood flow. The computer has identified this poorly flowing blood by use of red diamonds and downward red arrows. Decreased blood flow in the brain will diminish oxygen levels to the cranial tissues. This angiogram demonstrates some of the adverse effects of the radiation emitted by cellular phones.

The angiogram demonstrating the blood flow findings from the effects of the cell phone use with the MRET-Shield in place is startling. Initially, it can be seen that there is a strong similarity between the control findings and the MRET protected cell phone values, however closer examination reveals an even more interesting result. The subject talking on the cellular phone protected with an MRET-Shield has an increased blood flow compared to that demonstrated by the control values. Mere observation reveals far more yellow octagons in the MRET-Shield protected results than the control, indicating an increased blood flow when talking on an MRET-Shield protected cell phone.

When this information was presented in Vancouver one month after the results were released, a very astute nurse questioned me after the three sets of slides were presented. "Dr. Fisher, are you saying we should give our children cell phones with MRET-Shield chips on them."

I was somewhat shocked by the statement and I carefully reversed my slides, examining the control slide and the MRET-Shield slide. After a moment, I boldly announced, "I guess I am!"

## <u>FIGURE XXXV</u>
## <u>MAGNETIC RESONANCE ANGIOGRAM</u>
## <u>ACTIVE CELL PHONE WITH MRET CHIP</u>

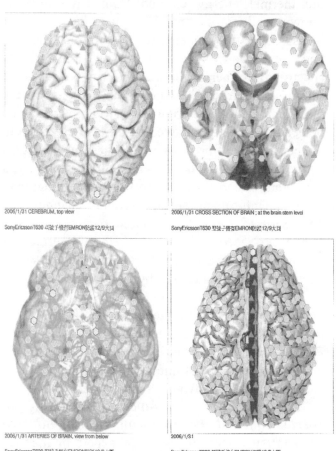

2006/1/31 CEREBRUM, top view

SonyEricssonT630 此號手機有EMRON防護12/9大圖

2006/1/31 CROSS SECTION OF BRAIN ; at the brain stem level

SonyEricssonT630 型號手機有EMRON防護12/9大圖

2006/1/31 ARTERIES OF BRAIN, view from below

SonyEricssonT630 型號手機有EMRON防護12/9大圖

2006/1/31

SonyEricssonT630 型號手機有EMRON防護12/9大圖

呂青宏博士 適性過量細胞營養健康中心

## THERMOGRAPHY

Subtle changes in heat content of tissue may only be perceivable to a minimal portion of the population that is either heat sensitive or electrically hypersensitive. The ability to detect and measure the thermal energy emitted from any object is known as thermography. The instruments used to measure the thermal energy are infrared cameras, and these cameras convert the invisible infrared spectrum into thermal images that can be translated into a photograph. Many wavelengths of the electromagnetic spectrum are too long to be detected by the human eye and these are referred to as thermal or infrared energy. These wavelengths are perceived by the body as heat. Everything has a temperature, and through the use of thermography the temperature, and any temperature changes, can be measured using the infrared camera. The images produced clearly show the heating effects of the infrared or "heat" radiation and not surprisingly show us the heating caused by cellular phones.

Recently I had the pleasure of meeting a multi-disciplinary physician from Hawaii, Dr. Linda Fickes. Not only is she a Doctor of Chiropractic and a certified clinical nutritionist, but this multiple cum laude graduate from Michigan State University is a member of **the American Academy of Thermology and the American Medical Infrared Association**. Dr. Fickes is an expert in medical thermography. I would like to thank her for several of the thermography images displayed in this book.

From these following images, one will totally grasp both the bio-heating affects of cellular phones and the tremendous ability of the MRET-Shield polymer to not only negate these deleterious effects but perhaps even show overall physiological improvements.

The images of the forty-five year-old woman that follow were captured in January 2007 by Dr. Fickes.

**FIGURE XXXVI**
**THERMOGRAPHY**
**CONTROL**

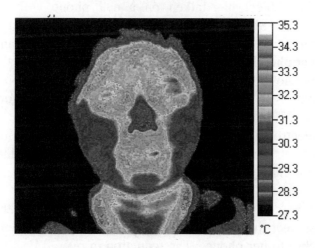

From this image one can note that there is excessive heat surrounding the sinus cavities and the teeth. In the next image (Figure XXXVII) the subject had been talking on an unprotected cell phone for fifteen minutes. It can be seen that there is an increase in temperature in all areas of the face and a much more pervasive overall heating in the lateral regions of the face.  Note the area of the right ear, the left eye and down throughout the neck, including the area around the thyroid gland.  These areas have sustained a significant temperature increase, but the real threat that should be considered is the fact that these areas demonstrated a temperature increase at all.  What other cellular damage may have been done by this radiation?  One must be aware that thermal effects are only one aspect of the radiation damage.  There are more.

In the following image (Figure XXXVIII), the subject has talked on a cell phone with an MRET-Shield polymer chip.  There has been a reduction of heat in all areas of the sinuses, face and peripheral areas, not only when compared to the previous image (talking on an unprotected phone) but even when compared to the control (Figure XXXVI).  These findings raise the issue of electromagnetic radiation (EMR) bioaccumulation effects, when considering that this individual normally uses a cell phone.

Figure XXXIX shows the image of the subject thirty days after applying an MRET-Shield chip to her phone.  The reduction in overall heating has continued and there has been a further decrease in the area of the cervical lymph nodes.  The significance of this finding relates not only to the immediate electromagnetic noise field affects

## FIGURE XXXVII
## THERMOGRAPHY
## CELL PHONE

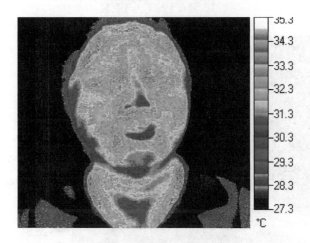

## FIGURE XXXVIII
## THERMOGRAPHY
## CELL PHONE WITH MRET CHIP

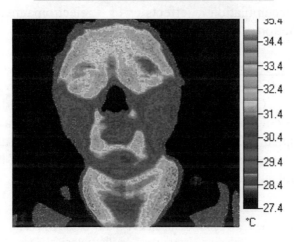

### FIGURE XXXIX
### THERMOGRAPHY
### CELL PHONE WITH MRET CHIP
### 30 DAYS LATER

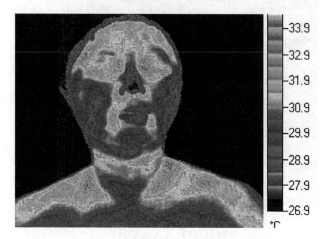

induced by the MRET-Shield polymer,[240] but also to the potential of the polymer to reverse the bioaccumulation effects of electromagnetic radiation.

## SAR (SPECIFIC ABSORPTION RATE)

Governmental agencies around the world, including the FCC in the United States, have adopted what they deem to be limits for safe exposure to the electromagnetic fields given off by cellular phones and devices, otherwise known as

---

[240]Smirnov I V. (2005) Comparative Study of the Effect of Microwave Radiation Neutralizers on Physiological State of Human Subjects. *Explore Magazine*. 2005;(14)5: p.29-44.

radiofrequency (RF) energy. These limits, which many of the top researchers in the world consider to be set to unrealistically high standards[241] are given in terms of a unit referred to as the Specific Absorption Rate (SAR). SAR is a measure of the amount of radio frequency energy absorbed by the body when using a mobile phone. The FCC requires that all cell phone manufacturers ensure that their phones comply with these objective limits for what they deem to be safe exposure levels. Every cellular phone sold in any country that has adopted these regulatory values must be below these SAR levels. The FCC limit for exposure from cellular telephones is a SAR level of 1.6 watts per kilogram (1.6 W/kg) and in Europe the value is 2.0 watts per kilogram (2.0 W/kg).

The SAR evaluation was conducted at the RF Exposure Lab in Escondido, California on two models of the RF (radio frequency) mobile phones with a functioning frequency of 836 MHz and three models of cellular phones with a functioning frequency of 1880 MHz. In compliance with SAR testing methodology the experiments were conducted on a "phantom head" filled with water based jelly simulating brain tissue. In every test situation the SAR values were measured in two hundred and forty-two points on the "phantom

---

[241] Sage C, Carpenter D, Eds. BioInitiative Report: A Rationale for a Biologically-based Public Exposure Standard for Electromagnetic Fields (ELF and RF). BioInitiative Working Group. USA. August 31, 2007.

# FIGURE XL
# SAR TESTING HOT SPOTS
# CONTROL

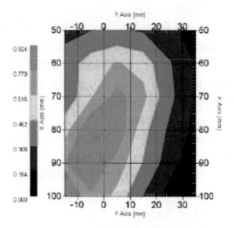

# FIGURE XLI
# SAR TESTING HOT SPOTS
# MRET POLYMER

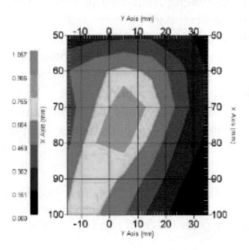

head". When comparing the control values against the MRET-Shield application to the cellular phone, all of the 'hot spots' remained in the same physical sites, however there was a decrease in SAR in ninety-percent (90%) of the recorded locations. The application of MRET-Shield polymer to the radiofrequency cell phones revealed the overall reduction of meaningful SAR values in these experiments in the range of 0.3% – 29.0%. Furthermore the application of the MRET-Shield does not lead to any significant distortion of transmitted RF signals.

Figures XL and XLI represent the "Hot Spot" Area Scan diagrams. From these it can clearly be seen that the application of the MRET Shield polymer to the cell phone did not change the location of the "Hot Spot" and also significantly decreased the SAR values in the scanned areas.

## MRET SHIELD IN VITRO TESTING ON HUMAN BLOOD CELLS

Testing was conducted at the Cedar Sinai Medical Center in Los Angeles under the auspices of Dr. Michael Newman. Twenty-two blood samples were studied and each sample was divided into three parts: a control sample that was not exposed to any radiation, a sample exposed to the radiation of a fourteen (14) inch computer display screen for one hour, and a sample that was exposed to the same computer monitor for one hour but with an MRET-Shield device in place.

## FIGURE XLII
## EMR EFFECT ON GRANULOCYTE COUNT

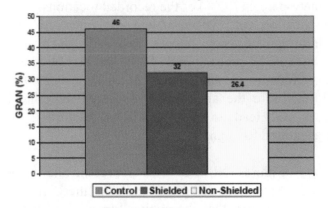

## FIGURE XLIII
## EMR EFFECT ON LYMPHOCYTE COUNT

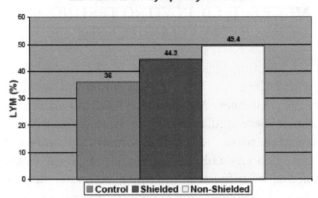

Full blood work was conducted and the overall values demonstrated statistically significant findings. This experiment revealed that the installation of MRET-Shield on computer monitor reduced the level of combined changes in the content of White Blood Cells (WBC) count, the protective elements of the immune system, by twenty-nine percent (29%).

WBC counts are measured to test the ability of the subject to respond to infection, confirm presence of infection, to indicate the type of infection, to give feedback to the response to treatment for infection or the side effects of therapy, and monitor for complications of illness. Granulocytes are white blood cells that are a key component of blood and play one of the most important roles in the immune system reaction. A decrease in granulocytes is indicative of decreased immune system function, as one of the roles of this cell type is to respond to inflammation and clean up debris (phagocytosis). The testing showed a decrease of granulocytes caused by the computer monitor radiation (Figure XLII) and that by using the MRET polymer, the EMF effects were diminished by twenty-nine percent (29%).

Figure XLIII reveals the radiation effects on lymphocytes. An increase in the lymphocyte count is associated with a physiological response to an antigenic or inflammatory stimulus and infection or other kind of external stress. The general consensus is that the increase of lymphocytes above normal level in case of the absence of any infections increases the risk of leukemia, lymphomas, and other disorders. The experiment revealed the increase of lymphocytes in blood samples exposed to the computer monitor radiation. It also showed that the installation of MRET-Shield on the computer monitor reduced the level of changes in lymphocyte count by thirty-eight percent (38%).

This experiment provides evidence that the exposure of human blood samples *in vitro* to EMR of the computer monitor affects the ratio of granulocytes and lymphocytes in the WBC. This effect is related to the stress response and can affect cellular processes related to the blood morphology such as growth, division and death of cells in all types of white blood cells. The installation of MRET-Shield on the computer monitor significantly reduced the effect of EMR on the ratio of WBC components (by 29%) and on the blood morphology.

# CHAPTER 6

# KNOWLEDGE IS THE SEED

*Science knows no country, because knowledge belongs to humanity, and is the torch which illuminates the world. Science is the highest personification of the nation because that nation will remain the first which carries the furthest the works of thought and intelligence.*

*Louis Pasteur*

Man's pursuit of knowledge and information has always been filled with those that choose to refute and challenge a set of facts both before and after the evidence has been demonstrated. This is not new. They told Columbus that the world was flat and that he would fall off of the edge long before he set out to discover another route to India and landed in Central America. No one ever believed that Alexander Graham Bell could send a signal down a wire and have it heard on the other end, and yet he pioneered the transmission of information that has progressed to the point where the wires are no longer needed. They told the Wright brothers that if man were meant to fly he would have wings and that any man-made structure would be too heavy to ever get off of the ground. All of these individuals persevered in light of adversity to bring about a new knowledge and base of understanding.

When Columbus sailed there were many who did not believe that he had arrived anywhere until he returned with the inhabitants of the newly discovered lands. The same with Bell until people actually heard the distant voice come through his telephone. With flying, all it took was one look and the evidence was clear, however there are those who are very unsure as to whether Neil Armstrong actually walked on the moon. There will always be people who are skeptical about anything and that is why proof is important.

There are many people that do not believe that EMFs and microwave radiation are dangerous at all. Sadly their lack of belief will not protect them from the proven physiological effects. Fortunately there is now a body of scientific information. Researchers have conducted enough investigations to demonstrate to those that deny the existence of the problem that there is indeed a dose-response relationship between diseases and electromagnetic radiation.[242]   A major group of scientists has just released a call for action based on their understanding of the problem.[243]

---

[242] Fisher H W. The Invisible Threat: The Risks Associated With EMFs. Wood Publishing. Toronto. 2007.
[243] Sage C, Carpenter D, Eds. BioInitiative Report: A Rationale for a Biologically-based Public Exposure Standard for Electromagnetic Fields (ELF and RF). BioInitiative Working Group. USA. August 31, 2007.

The knowledge of the risks and potential health threats we face from a plethora of causes has brought about our current health status. We must take any action that we can to improve our health to move forward into the future. It is the top scientists and physicians who will lead the way and their acceptance of the realities, both positive and negative, is of major importance. These individuals are amongst the first to be exposed to this new information about the benefits of MRET Technology and the unique abilities that can serve mankind.

The MRET activation and subsequent ingestion of water will affect the permeability at the cellular membrane level producing a number of beneficial physiological functions. The installation of the MRET-Shield polymer chip significantly reduces the effects and damages caused by electromagnetic fields. These benefits are undeniable as you have seen from the evidence presented in this book. At distinguished conferences around the world this information has been disseminated with open acceptance. Several of these conferences are listed below:

Dr. Fisher "Electro Magnetic Radiation and Mobile Phones – New dimensions." Moolchand Medicity Hospital and the Indian Medical Association, New Delhi. February 23, 2008.

16th International Biophysics Congress (IUPAB), February 2-6, 2008, Long Beach, California, USA. Program and Abstract Book, Dr. Smirnov: "The

Effect of MRET Activated Water on Microbiological Culture *Escherichia coli* K-12 and on Complex Microbiological Associations."

BioPro Convention, January 6, 2008, La Jolla, CA. USA. Oral presentation, Dr. Fisher: "The Risks Associated With Electromagnetic Radiation and the Protection Effects of MRET Technology."

15th Annual World Congress On Anti-Aging Medicine & Regenerative Biomedical Technologies December 15, 2007, Las Vegas, Nevada. Oral presentation Dr. Fisher "The Physiological Benefits of Increasing Cellular Membrane Permeability."

SEMAL Anti-Ageing Conference of Spain. Barcelona. September 30, 2007. Oral Presentation Dr. Fisher: "The Risks Associated With Electromagnetic Fields"

SEMAL Anti-Ageing Conference of Spain. Barcelona. September 29, 2007. Oral Presentation, Dr. Fisher "The Physiological Benefits of Improving Cellular Membrane Permeability"

4th Annual Anti-Ageing Conference London 2007, The Royal Society of Medicine, London, England, September 13, 2007. Oral presentation Dr. Fisher, "The Risks Associated With Electromagnetic Fields."

International Microwave Power Institute, 41st Annual International Microwave Symposium,

Vancouver, BC, Canada, August 1-3, 2007. Oral presentation, Dr. Smirnov: "MRET Fractal Matrix and its Effect on SAR Values of RF Phones".

15th Annual World Congress On Anti-Aging Medicine & Regenerative Biomedical Technologies August 1, 2007, Chicago, Illinois, USA. Oral presentation Dr. Fisher, "The Invisible Threat: The Risks Associated with EMFs."

Bioelectromagnetic Society Annual Meeting, June 11-15, 2007, Kanazawa, Japan. Program and Abstract Book, Dr. Smirnov: "MRET Activated Water and Its Successful Application for Prevention Treatment and Enhanced Tumor Resistance in Animal Oncology Models"

Rutgers Symposium on Lunar Settlements, June 3-8, 2007, New Brunswick, NJ, USA. Oral Presentation Dr. Smirnov. "Treatment and Enhanced Tumor Resistance in Animal Oncology Models"

BioPro Convention, January 5, 2007, Palm Desert, USA. Oral presentation, Dr. Smirnov: "The Effect of MRET-Shield on Electromagnetic Radiation."

The Society for Physical Regulation in Biology and Medicine, 24th Scientific Conference, January 11-13, 2006, Cancun, Mexico. Program and Abstract Book, Dr. Smirnov: "Electrically Activated Water."

National Cancer Center, December 14, 2005, Bangkok, Thailand. Oral presentation, Dr. Smirnov: "MRET-Shield Polymer Material Protecting Biological Systems against EMR."

Thailand National TV Channel 11, December 15, 2005, Bangkok, Thailand. Press Conference, Dr. Smirnov: "The Physiological Effect of MRET Activated Water on Patients Suffering from AIDS".

Bangkok Medical Association, December 15, 2005, Bangkok, Thailand. Scientific Seminar, Dr. Smirnov: "MRET Activated Water Physiological Effects".

Thailand Ministry of Public Health and The Chemistry Society of Thailand, April 2005, Bangkok, Thailand. Scientific Seminar. Dr. Smirnov: "Nanotechnology invention: Molecular Resonance Effect technology."

The Bioelectromagnetic Society 26th Annual Meeting, June 20-24, 2004, Washington D.C., USA. Program and Abstract Book, Dr. Smirnov: "Method, Material and Device Providing Electromagnetic Compatibility Between Technologically Originated EMR and Biological Systems."

"Long-term Water Memory Effect and its Technological Implementation and Benefits" - April 20-22, 2004, Seoul, Korea. Oral presentation Dr. Smirnov.

Asia-Pacific Electromagnetic Fields Conference, January 2004, Bangkok, Thailand. Program and Abstract Book, Dr. Smirnov: "Method, Material and Device Providing Electromagnetic Compatibility between Technologically Originated EMR and Biological Systems."

Anti-Aging International Conference. September 2003, Singapore. Oral Presentation, Dr. Smirnov: "Physics of MRET water."

The First Asia and Oceanic Congress for Radiation Protection, October 2002, Seoul, Korea. Program and Abstract Book, Dr. Smirnov: "Electromagnetic Radiation Optimum Neutralizer."

Anti-Aging International Conference, June 2002, Singapore. Oral Presentation, Dr. Smirnov: "Molecular Resonance Effect Technology."

Effects of EMR on Biological Systems, Scientific Conference, Taipei, Taiwan, August 2000. Oral Presentation, Dr. Smirnov: "MRET-Shield - shielding material and device."

Many more congresses and conferences will be attended and the pertinent information delivered for the consideration of those in attendance. This information must be disseminated for the public good. At the time of this writing there will be at least six presentations at highly esteemed conferences on at least three continents around the world to inform  them, not only about the potential problems we are facing, but about the solutions available using MRET technology. We can change the world, one person at a time.

# BIBLIOGRAPHY

Ahlbom A, Green A, Kheifets L, Savitz D, Swerdlow A. Epidemiology of health effects of radiofrequency exposure. *Environ Health Perspect.* 2004; 112:p.1741-1754.

Andreassi L, Flori L. Mineral water and spas in Italy. Clinics in Dermatology. 1996;(14)6:p. 627-632.

Arnetz B B, Berg M. Melatonin and adrenocorticotropic hormone levels in video display unit workers during work and leisure. *J Occup Med.* 1996; 38(11):p1108-1110.

Arnetz B B, Akerstedt T, Hillert L, Lowden A, Kuster N, Wiholm C. The Effects of 884 MHz GSM Wireless Communication Signals on Self-reported Symptom and Sleep (EEG)- An Experimental Provocation Study. Piers Online. 2007;3(7):p.1148-1150.

Aw S T, Todd M J, McGarvie L A, Migliaccio A A, Halmagyi G M. Effects of Unilateral Vestibular Deafferentation on the Linear Vestibulo-Ocular Reflex Evoked by Impulsive Eccentric Roll Rotation. *J Neurophysiol.* 2003;89: p.969-978.

Batmanghelidj F. Your Body's Many Cries for Water: A Preventive and Self-Education Manual for Those Who Prefer to Adhere to the Logic of the

Natural and the Simple in Medicine. Global Health Solutions. Falls Church, VA. 1995.

Begley S. "The End of Antibiotics". Newsweek. 1994; Mar. 28: p.46-51.

Bellavite P, Signorini A. Biological Effects of Electromagnetic Fields. Institute of Clinical Chemistry and Microscopy. University of Verona, 2003.

Berg J M, Tymoczko J L, Stryer L. Biochemistry 5th Edition. W. H. Freeman. New York. 2002.

Brady J V, Reiter R J. Neurobehavioral effects. In: Health Effects of Low-Frequency Electric and Magnetic Fields. Report to the Committee on Interagency Radiation Research and Policy Coordination; Oak Ridge Associated Universities Panel. NTIS Publication #029-000-00443-9: VII-1-VII-56. 1992.

Burch J B, Reif J S, Noonan C W, Yost M G. Melatonin metabolite levels in workers exposed to 60 Hz magnetic fields: work in substations and with 3-phase conductors. J Occup Envir Med. 2000; 42:p136-142.

Carlo G, Schram M. Cell Phones: Invisible Hazards in the Wireless Age. Carroll & Graf Publishers. New York. 2001; p.111.

Davis S, Mirick D K, Chen C, Stanczyk F Z. Effects of 60-Hz magnetic field exposure on nocturnal 6-Sulfatoxymelatonin, estrogens, luteinizing hormone, and follicle-stimulating hormone in healthy reproductive age women: Results of a crossover trials. *Ann Epidemiol* 2006; 16 (8): 622 – 631.

Dunning, B.F. "Rydberg Atoms - Giants of the Atomic *World Science Spectra*. 1995;(3): 34-38, 1995.

Emoto M, Thayne T A (translator). The Hidden Messages In Water. Beyond Words Publishing. Hillsboro, Ore 2004.

Epstein C M. *Introduction to EEG and evoked potentials*. J. B. Lippincot Co. Philadelphia. 1983. Epstein S S. The Stop Cancer Before it Starts Campaign. Chicago. The Cancer prevention Coalition. 2003;p.12.

Fisher H W. Reishi Rescue: R & R for Your Immune System. Wood Publishing. Toronto. 2005;p.30.

Fisher H W. The Invisible Threat: The Risks Associated With EMFs. Wood Publishing. Toronto. 2007.

Gallagher T F, Beams J W. Rydberg Atoms. Cambridge University Press. New York. 1994; p120-135.

Gandhi G A. Genetic damage in mobile phone users: some preliminary findings. *Indian J Hum Genet.* 2005;11:p.99-104.

Gandhi G A, Singh P. Mobile phone users: Another high health risk group. *J Hum Ecol.* 2005; 18(2):p.85-92.

Grota L J, Reiter R J, Keng P, Michaelson S. Electric field exposure alters serum melatonin but not pineal melatonin synthesis in male rats. *Bioelectromagnetics.* 1994; 15:p427-437.

Hamblin D L, Wood A W. Effects of mobile phone emissions on human brain activity and sleep variables. *Int J Radiat Biol.* 2002; 78:p.659-669.

Hamblin D L, Wood A W, Croft R J, Stough C. Examining the effects of electromagnetic fields emitted by GSM mobile phones on human event-related potentials and performance during an auditory task. *Clin Neurophysiol.* 2004; 115:p.171-178.

Hayden J E. Adventures on the Dark Side: An Introduction to Darkfield Microscopy. *BioTechniques.* 2002; 32(4): p.756-761.

Head-Gordon T, Johnson M E. Tetrahedral structure or chains for liquid water. *PNAS.* 2006; (103)21: p. 7973-7977.

149

Hillert L, Berglind N, Arnetz B B, Bellander T. Prevalence of self-reported hypersensitivity to electric magnetic fields in a population-based questionnaire survey. *Scand j Work Environ Health.* 2002; 28(1):p33-41.

Hillman D. Exposure to electric and magnetic fields (EMF) linked to neuro-endocrine stress syndrome: increased cardiovascular disease, diabetes and cancer. *Shocking News.* 2005; (8):p2.

Hocking B. Preliminary report: Symptoms associated with mobile phone use. *Occ Med.* 1998; 48(6):p.357-360.

Hyland G J. The Physiological and Environmental Effects of Non-ionizing Electromagnetic Radiation. Private Treaty No. EP/IV/A/STOA/2000/07/03, University of Warwick. 2001.

Katz M, Amit I, Citri A, Shay T, Carvalho S, Lavi S, Milanezi F, Lyass L, Amariglio N, Jacob-Hirsch J, Ben-Chetrit N, Tarcic G, Lindzen M, Avraham R, Liao Y C, Trusk P, Lyass A, Rechavi G, Spector N L, Lo S H, Schmitt F, Bacus S S, Yarden Y. A reciprocal tensin-3–cten switch mediates EGF-driven mammary cell migration. *Nature Cell Biology.* 2007; 9:p.961-969.

Kholodna L S. The Effect of MRET Activated Water on Staphylococcus Infections in vivo in Animal Model and in vitro on Staphylococcus aureus Wood-46 Culture. Biological Department of

Kyiv National Taras Shevchenko University. Kyiv. 2007.

Jacoby G A. "Antimicrobial-resistant pathogens in the 1990s". Annu Rev Med. 1996; 47: p.169-79.

Jones R R. Modifying Atomic Architecture. Science Spectra, 2000;(22): p.52-59.

Kato M, Honma K, Shigemitsu T, Shiga Y. Circularly polarized 50-Hz magnetic field exposure reduces pineal gland melatonin and blood concentrations of long-evans rats. *Neuroscience Letters.* 1994; 166:p59-62.

Kato M, Honma K, Shigemitsu T, Shiga Y. Effects of exposure to a circularly polarized 50-Hz magnetic field on plasma and pineal melatonin levels in rats. *Bioelectromagnetics.* 1993; 14:p97-110.

Katz M, Amit I, Citri A, Shay T, Carvalho S, Lavi S, Milanezi F, Lyass L, Amariglio N, Jacob-Hirsch J, Ben-Chetrit N, Tarcic G, Lindzen M, Avraham R, Liao Y C, Trusk P, Lyass A, Rechavi G, Spector N L, Lo S H, Schmitt F, Bacus S S, Yarden Y. A reciprocal tensin-3–cten switch mediates EGF-driven mammary cell migration. *Nature Cell Biology.* 2007; 9:p.961-969.

Koivisto M, Revonsuo A, Krause C, Haarala C, Sillanmäki L, Laine M, Hämäläinen H. Effects of 902 MHz electromagnetic field emitted by cellular telephones on response times in humans. *Neuroreport.* 2000; 11(2):p.413-15.

Krause C M, Harrala C, Sillanmäki L, Koivisto M, Alnko K, Reyonsuo A, Laine M, Hämäläinen H. Effects of electromagnetic field emitted by cellular phones on the EEG during an auditory memory task: a double blind replication study. *Bioelectromagnetics.* 2004; 25:p.33-40.

Lai H, Singh H P. Single and double strand DNA breaks in rat brain cells after acute exposure to radiofrequency electromagnetic radiation *Int J Radiat Biol.* 1996; 69:p.513-521.

Lai H, Singh N P. Acute low-intensity microwave exposure increases DNA single-strand breaks in rat brain cells. *Bioelectromagnetics.* 1995; 16:p.207-210.

Li C, Jiang H, Fu Y. A study on dose-effect of suppression to gap junctional intercellular communication function by 50-Hz magnetic fields] Zhonghua Yu Fang Yi Xue Za Zhi. 1998;32(3): p.142-4. Chinese.

Ling G N. A New Theoretical Foundation for the Polarized-Oriented Multilayer Theory of Cell Water and for Inanimate Systems Demonstrating Long-range Dynamic Structuring of Water Molecules. *Physiol Chem Phys & Med NMR.* 2003; 35: p.91-130.

Litovitz T A, Montrose C J, Doinov P, Brown K M, Barber M. Superimposing spatially coherent electromagnetic noise inhibits field-induced abnormalities in developing chick embryos. *Bioeletromagnetics.* 1994;15(2):p.105-13.

Litovitz T A, Penafiel L M, Farrel J M, Krause D, Meister R, Mullins J M.Bioeffects induced by exposure to microwaves are mitigated by superposition of ELF noise. *Bioelectromagnetics.* 1997; 18(6):p.422-30.

Litovitz T A, Krause D, Montrose C J, Mullins J M. Temporally incoherent magnetic fields mitigate the response of biological systems to temporally coherent magnetic fields. *Bioelectromagnetics.* 1994; 15(5):p.399-409.

Maret K. Electromagnetic Fields and Human Health. National Foundation For Alternative Medicine. Washington, D.C. 2003; p13.

Mild, K H., Oftedal, G, Sandstrom M., Wilen J, Tynes T, Haugsdal B, Hauger E. Comparison of symptoms by users of analogue and digital mobile phones - A Swedish-Norwegian epidemiological study. *National Institute for Working Life*, Umea, Sweden. 1998; 23: p.84.

Neu H C. "The crisis in antibiotic resistance". Science. 1992; 257(5073): p.1064-73.

Philips A, Philips J. The Power Watch Handbook. Piatkus Books. London. 2006; p.294.

Reiter R J, Anderson L E, Buschbom R L, Wilson B W. Reduction of the nocturnal rise in pineal melatonin levels in rats exposed to 60-Hz electric fields in utero and for 23 days after birth. *Life Science.* 1988; 42:p2203-2206.

Reiter R J, Tan D X, Pappolla M A. Melatonin relieves the neural oxidative burden that contributes to dementias. *Ann N Y Acad Sci.* 2004; 1035:p179-196.

Rogers W R, Reiter R J, Smith H D, Barlow-Walden L. Rapid-onset/offset, variably scheduled 60 Hz electric and magnetic field exposure reduces nocturnal serum melatonin concentration in nonhuman primates. *Bioelectromagnetics.* 1995; S3:119-122.

Sage C, Carpenter D, Eds. BioInitiative Report: A Rationale for a Biologically-based Public Exposure Standard for Electromagnetic Fields (ELF and RF). BioInitiative Working Group. USA. August 31, 2007.

Schernhammer E S, Hankinson S E. Urinary melatonin levels and breast cancer risk. *J Natl Cancer Inst.* 2005; 97(14):p1084-1087.

Schernhammer E S, Laden F, Speizer F E, Willett W C, Hunter D J, Kawachi I, Fuchs C S, Colditz G A: Night-shift work and risk of colorectal cancer in the Nurses' Health Study. *J Natl Cancer Inst.* 2003; 95(11): p825-828.

Salem A A, Mossa H A, Barsoum B N. Application of nuclear magnetic resonance spectroscopy for quantitative analysis of miconazole, metronidazole and sulfamethoxazole in pharmaceutical and urine samples. J of Pharmaceutical & Biomedical Analysis. 2006; 41(2):p.654-661.

Salford L G, Brun A, Sturesson K, Eberhardt J L, Persson B R. Permeability of the blood-brain barrier induced by 915 MHz electromagnetic radiation, continuous wave and modulated at 8, 16, 50, and 200 Hz. Microsc Res Tech. 1994; 27(6):p.535-42.

Selmaoui B, Touitou Y. Sinusoidal 50-Hz magnetic fields depress rat pineal NAT activity and serum melatonin. Role of duration and intensity of exposure. *Life Science.* 1995; 57:p1351-1358.

Semikhina L P, Kiselev V F. Effect of weak magnetic fields on the properties of water and ice. *Russian Physics Journal.* 1988;(31)5:p.351-354.

Singh N P, McCoy M T, Tice R R, Schneider E L. A simple technique for quantitation of low levels of DNA damage in individual cells. *Exp Cell Res.* 1988;175:p.184-91.

Singh S. "With 83m additions in a year, India fastest growing cell mkt." *The Times Of India.* Saturday February 16, 2008;p.21.

Smirnov, I. "Activated Water," *Explore Magazine.* 2002;(11).2.

Smirnov I. Activated Water. *Electronic Journal of Biotechnology.* 2003;(6)2:p.128-142.

Smirnov I V. The Anomalous Low Viscosity and Polarized-Oriented Multilayer Structure of MRET Activated Water. *Explore Magazine.* 2007;(16):4:p.37-39.

Smirnov I V. The Effect of MRET Activated Water on Microbiological Culture Escherichia coli K-12 and on Complex Microbiological Associations. *Explore Magazine.* 2008; 17(1):p.1-6.

Smirnov I V. MRET Activated Water and its Successful Application for Preventive Treatment and Enhanced Tumor Resistance in Oncology. *European Journal of Scientific Research.* 2007;(16)4: p.575-583.

Smirnov I V. Mechanism of Possible Biological Effect of Activated Water on Patients Suffering from Alzheimer's Disease. *Explore Magazine.* 2006;5:p.53-56.

Smirnov I V. The Physiological Effect of MRET Activated Water on Patients Suffering from AIDS. *Explore Magazine.* 2006; (15)2:p.37-40.

Smirnov I V, Peerayot T. The Physiological Effect of MRET Activated Water. *Explore Magazine*. 2006;(15)1: p.38-44.

Smirnov, I.V. (2006) "Clinical Observation by Peerayot Trongsawad, M. D., Using MRET-Activated Water as Additional Treatment" *Explore Magazine*. 2006;(14)6.

Smirnov I V. The Possible Effect of MRET Activated Water on Diabetic Patients. *Explore Magazine*. 2005;(14)2:p.49-54.

Smirnov I V. The Effect of a Specially Modified Electromagnetic Field on the Molecular Structure of Liquid Water. *Explore Magazine*. 2004; (13):1.

Smirnov I V. Mechanism of Activated Water's Biological Effect on Viruses. *Explore Magazine*. 2003; (12)4:p.34-36.

Smirnov I V. Activated Water. *Electric Spacecraft Journal*. 2002;33:p.15-17.

Smirnov I V. Polymer Material Providing Compatibility between Technologically Originated EMR and Biological Systems. *Explore Magazine*. 2006; (15)4:p.26-32.

Smirnov I V. (2005) Comparative Study of the Effect of Microwave Radiation Neutralizers on Physiological State of Human Subjects. *Explore Magazine*. 2005;(14)5: p.29-44.

Smirnov I V. Electromagnetic Radiation Optimum Neutralizer. *Explore Magazine.*, 2002;(11)1: p.45-50.

Smirnov I V. Electromagnetic Radiation Optimum Neutralizer. *RSO Magazine* (Radiation Safety Associates). December, 2001.

Sonnier H, Marino A A. Sensory Transduction as a Proposed Model for Biological Detection of Electro-magnetic Fields. *Electro and Magnetobiology.* 2001; 20(2): p.153-175.

Stevens R.G, Wilson B W, Anderson L E. The Melatonin Hypothesis: Breast cancer and the use of electric power. Columbus, Ohio: Battelle Press. 1997.

Stevens R G. Re: Risk of postmenopausal breast cancer and use of electric blankets. *Am J Epi* 1995; 142:p146.

Sullivan F W, Gentile K, Boelhouwer C. Relationship of Clinical Symptomatology to Abnormal EEG Findings: A Family Study. *Am J Psychiatry.* 1967;124:p.554-559.

Sun W, Fu Y, Jiang H, Lu D. The Clustering of Growth Factor and Cytokine Factor Receptors Was Induced by 50 Hz Magnetic Field and Blocked by Noise Magnetic Field.

Tennenbaum J. Russian Scientists Replicate 'Impossible' Mitogenetic Radiation. 21st Century Science & Technology.Winter 2000-2001: p.60-63.

Thatcher R W, North D, Biver C. EEG and intelligence: relations between EEG coherence, EEG phase delay and power. *Clin Neurophysiol.* 2005;116(9):p.2129-41.

Truong H, Yellon S M. Effect of various acute 60 Hz magnetic field exposures on the nocturnal melatonin rise in the adult Djungarian hamster. *Journal of Pineal Research.* 1997; 22:p.177-183.

United Nations Scientific Committee on the Effects of Atomic Radiation. Sources and Effects of Ionizing Radiation:   UNSCEAR 1993 Report to the General Assembly, with Scientific Annexes. 1993.

Vijayalaxmi B Z, Frei M R, Dusch S J, Guel V, Meltz M L, Jauchem J R. Frequency of micronuclei in the peripheral blood and bone marrow of cancer-prone mice chronically exposed to 2450 MHz radiofrequency radiation. *Radiation Research.* 1997a; 147: p495-500.

Villeneuve P J, Agnew D A, et al. Non-Hodgkin's lymphoma among electric utility workers in Ontario: the evaluation of alternative indices of exposure to 60Hx electric and magnetic fields. *Occup Environ Med.* 2000; 57:349-357.

Vysotskii V I, Smirnov I V, Kornilova A A. Introduction to the Biophysics of Activated Water. Universal Publishers. Boca Raton, FLA. 2005.

Vysotskii V I. Experimental Observation and the Biophysical Model of Strong Germicidal Activity of Water Activated with the help of MRET Process and Investigation of Physical Properties of MRET Activated Water and its Successful Application for Prophylaxis and Treatment of Oncology. Program and Abstract Book, International Congress on Medical Physics and Biomedical Engineering, August 27 – September 1, 2006, Seoul, Korea.

Wenzel R P, Edmond M B. "The Impact of Hospital-Acquired Bloodstream Infections." Emerging Infectious Diseases. Vol. 7, No. 2. Mar-Apr 2001.

Wertheimer N, Leeper E. Adult cancer related to electrical wires near the home. *Int J Epidemiol.* 1982; 11:p345-355.

Wilson B W, Wright C W, Morris J F, Buschbom R L, Brown D P, Miller D L, Sommers-Flannigan R, Anderson L E. Evidence for an effect of elf electromagnetic fields on human pineal gland function. *Journal of Pineal Research.* 1990; 9:p259-269.

Wilson B W, Anderson L E, Hilton D I, Phillips R D. Chronic exposure to 60-Hz electric fields: Effects on pineal function in the rat. *Bioelectromagnetics.* 1981; 2:p371-380.

Wilson B W, Chess E K, Anderson L E. 60-Hz electric-field effects on pineal melatonin rhythms:

Time course for onset and recovery.
*Bioelectromagnetics*. 1986; 7:p239-242.

Wilson B W, Stevens R G, Anderson L E, eds.
<u>Extremely Low Frequency Electromagnetic Fields:</u>
<u>The Question of Cancer.</u> Columbus, OH (USA):
Battelle Press, 1990.

Yellon SM. Acute 60 Hz magnetic field exposure
effects on the melatonin rhythm in the pineal gland
and circulation of the adult Djungarian hamster.
*Journal of Pineal Research*. 1994; 16:p136-144.

Zeng Q, Chiang H, Fu Y, Lu D, Xu Z.
Electromagnetic noise blocks the gap-junctional
intercellular communication suppression induced by
50 Hz magnetic field] Zhonghua Lao Dong Wei
Sheng Zhi Ye Bing Za Zhi. 2002;20(4):p.243-5.
Chinese

Zeng Q, Ke Z, Gao X, Fu, Y, Lu D, Chiang H, Xu,
Z. Noise Magnetic Fields Abolish the Gap Junction
Intercellular Communication Suppression Induced
by 50 Hz Magnetic Fields. *Bioelectromagnetics*.
2006;27(4):p.274-9.

# ABOUT THE AUTHORS

Dr. Igor Smirnov, M.S., Ph.D.

Dr. Igor Smirnov graduated from St. Petersburg Naval Academy in 1975, Faculty of Nuclear Physics (Fission Reactors) and Engineering with a Master's of Science degree in mechanical engineering. Continuing his education into the next decade, he was actively involved in advanced research regarding the effects of low frequency electromagnetic oscillations (EMFs) on human cellular physiology at St. Petersburg State University, graduating in 1986 with his Ph.D. in Clinical Psychology.

His advanced research and study of the psychosomatic development of children swimming in infancy was conducted at St. Petersburg Children Hospital. The results of his research were

significant enough to be published by the World
Health Organization in Munich, Germany. His
research has been published in the St. Petersburg
University Press, and in peer reviewed magazines
such as Explore Magazine, The Electric Space Craft
Journal, The Electronic Journal of Biotechnology,
and The European Journal of Scientific Research.
Dr. Smirnov lectures extensively and makes
speaches at international scientific congresses and
conferences such as International Biophysics
Congress (2008), Anti-Aging International
Conferences (2003-2008), International Microwave
Symposium (2007), Bioelectromagnetic Society
Annual Meetings (2004-2007), Rutgers Symposium
on Lunar Settlements (2007), The Society for
Physical Regulation in Biology and Medicine
Conference (2006), Thailand National Cancer
Center Symposium (2005), Thailand Ministry of
Public Health and The Chemistry Society of
Thailand Meeting (2005), Asia-Pacific
Electromagnetic Fields Conference (2004), The
First Asia and Oceanic Congress for Radiation
Protection (2002), Effects of EMR on Biological
Systems Conference (2000). He is the President of
Global Quantech, Inc., a bio-technological research
company, and a Member of the Bioelectromagnetics
Society of America, the Biophysical Society and
the Association of American Engineers.

After the catastrophic nuclear plant radiation
leak at Chernobyl, Russia in 1986, which caused
more than three million cases of cancer, Dr.
Smirnov and his scientific team investigated the

normalizing effect of certain mountain spring water on victims of the radioactive fallout which lead to his invention of the molecular resonance effect technology. He has been awarded two United States patents "Method and Device for Producing Activated Liquids and Methods of Use Thereof" and "Electromagnetic Radiation Shielding Material and Device".

## Dr. Howard W. Fisher, B.Sc., B.Ed., D.C.

Dr. Howard W. Fisher, a prominent Toronto Natural Physician, is the founder and operator of the Glen Park Clinic. His clinic has special interests in sports injuries and nutrition. Dr. Fisher lectures internationally on anti-aging, nutrition, wellness, and immunology, and has written many articles for trade publications. His research has been published in peer-reviewed journals. He is a member of the scientific advisory board for several multinational nutraceutical companies and serves as a director for an Asian bio-tech company. Over the last year Dr. Fisher has lectured to thousands of medical doctors on the threat of electromagnetic fields.

Fisher is a member of the Canadian Chiropractic Association, the Ontario Chiropractic Association and the Canadian Chiropractic Protective Association. He has received an Award of Appreciation from the Canadian Chiropractic Association for the invention of the Back Strip, a spinal protective pad for contact sports.

Dr. Fisher received his B.Sc. and B.Ed. degrees from the University of Toronto and his Doctor of Chiropractic, cum laude, from the Canadian Memorial Chiropractic College in 1983. He is licensed to practice in the Province of Ontario and the State of Michigan.

In addition to his chiropractic career, Dr. Fisher is an avid athlete who still plays competitive hockey, and can be found on the golf course most afternoons. He has written more than a half a dozen screenplays, several commercials, a television series and is currently in pre-production for a feature length film.

A dynamic and colorful personality, Dr. Fisher resides in Thornhill, Ontario, Canada with his wife and two children.

## Other books by Dr. Howard W. Fisher

Wisdom of the Woods: Herbal Remedies

Extreme Toxic Times: How to Escape On Your Own Two Feet

Reishi Rescue: R & R for Your Immune System

Before You Breathe Deeply: The Immunological Significance of Breathing Purifying Air

Nature's Silver Bullet: Killing the Fear Factor

Reishi Response: Answering Today's Health Challenges

Approaching Wellness: Simple Steps to Restore Your Immune System

Enzymes and Your Health: Optimizing Your Physiological Functions

The Invisible Threat : The Risks Associated With EMFs

To find out more about Dr. Fisher's upcoming lectures or books go to www.fisherclinic.com

MINUTES 30    p.53

probiotic frequency waves   p.28
    (electromagnetic)

Effects p.70

30 MINUTES  p. 28

p.37 INHIBITION OF THE INFLAMATORY RESPONSE